BIOGRAPHY OF THE UNBORN

by Margaret Shea Gilbert

The revised edition of this book will be welcomed by everyone interested in the subject of human development.

This is a nontechnical account of the development of the human embryo and fetus, written specifically for the layman, illustrated with line drawings showing the stages of human development.

It will have special value for young women, and without a doubt, it is a must for those interested in nursing.

The style and manner of writing make it the needed bridge between highly technical medical school texts and basic works on general embryology. The very real danger of a woman causing malformation of her child through ignorance can be minimized by knowledge.

This is a book that no obstetrician would hesitate to recommend to pregnant women.

Biography of

THE UNBORN

By

Margaret Shea Gilbert

HAFNER PUBLISHING CO.
New York and London
1963

© Copyright 1962
Hafner Publishing Company, Inc.

Originally published 1938
Williams and Wilkins
—————
New revised edition 1962
Published by
HAFNER PUBLISHING COMPANY, INC.

Second Printing 1963

Library of Congress Catalog Card Number: 62-21746

Type set at THE POLYGLOT PRESS
Printed in the United States of America
at NOBLE OFFSET PRINTERS, INC.,
New York 3, New York

BIOGRAPHY OF THE UNBORN

For my daughters

Contents

ILLUSTRATIONS

PROLOGUE

THE LIFE OF MAN is a drama with many scenes, many moods, and many plots, played out by each man in the time allotted for his individual life. Man is in turn an embryo, fetus, infant, child, adolescent and adult, continuously changing in form and substance yet remaining individual and unique from his birth until his death. When a man is born, he is already nine months old, and during those first nine months of life each human being lives through a sequence of events and experiences that determine his unique nature and influence the course of his entire life after birth. The Chinese traditionally count the newborn human infant as being one year old at birth, adding this hidden stage of life to the known years that a man lives after birth. Each man's individual biography begins nine months before his birth, which is merely one event in the continuous series of changes that will characterize his entire life.

Ever since ancient times men have wondered and debated about how human life is started. The fact that sexual intercourse between the parents always precedes the creation of a child was perhaps the only real information known to primitive men. From this meager knowledge came the belief that woman was but the receptive soil in which the man sowed the seed that gives form, motion and soul to a new human being. In the play

7

Eumenides, Aeschylus has Apollo defend Orestes against the accusation of matricide by saying: "the mother is not the parent of her child, but nurse only of the young life that is sown in her. The male is the parent and she but a stranger, a friend, who if fate spares his plant, preserves it till it puts forth."

Not until the seventeenth century was it suggested by a Dutch physician, Rene de Graaf, that the woman supplied a definite and well-formed egg, similar in origin and purpose to the well-known egg of the bird, as the basis for the creation of a new human being. A Dutch lens maker, Anton Leeuwenhoek, first found in the semen of man the "little animals," or sperm, which are the essential contribution of the male to the creation of new life (Fig. 1). These two discoveries aroused a storm of dissension within the scientific world, a storm that raged for almost a century. There were two schools of scientists, the ovists and the spermists. The ovists claimed that the egg was the beginning of man, while the spermists claimed the same creative role for the sperm. Some imaginative men even believed that they saw a small but perfectly formed human fetus curled up within the sperm, which needed only to be implanted in the uterus of a woman where it could grow to full size. Not until the nineteenth century did men finally realize that the union of the sperm with the egg creates a new human being. This modern belief states that each living creature is created anew at the moment when the sperm of the father fuses with the egg of the mother in a process called fertilization.

But the question of how the extremely small and apparently simple egg and sperm can lead to the development of the relatively large and complex body of the newborn infant remained a mystery. Some scentists sug-

8

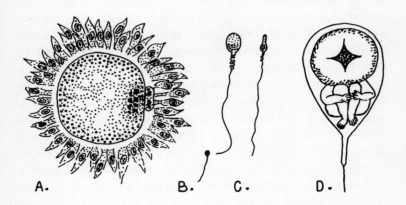

FIG. 1:

A. A mature human egg surrounded by nurse cells. The first polar body has been formed and the egg is ready for fertilization. Magnified 200 times.

B. A human sperm, drawn to about the same magnification as the egg in A.

C. Two human sperm, viewed from the flat side and on edge. The oval head of the sperm contains the chromosomal material of heredity; the middle piece contains a coiled filament that connects with the long, slender tail. Magnified about 800 times.

D. A seventeenth-century interpretation of the human sperm, showing the tiny fetus that was believed to be curled up in the head of the sperm. (Based on Arey.)

gested that the various organs of the body must be present, already formed but small in size, within either the egg or the sperm, and that these organs simply grow as a result of the absorption of food by the developing child from its mother. These men found it inconceivable that the complexity of the infant at birth could arise in any understandable way from the apparent simplicity of either the egg or the sperm, so they concluded that the human body had been preformed at the time of the original Creation and was passed on from generation to generation through the egg or sperm. This intriguing theory implied that all of the human beings that have ever lived in the long history of the earth had been contained, preformed and complete, within the bodies of their ancestors, one generation inside of the preceding generation like a series of Chinese boxes. The absurdity of this last assumption led other men to speculate that each new creature develops by a series of small changes that begin with the apparently simple egg and sperm, and lead, one step at a time, to the gradual formation of the many different cells, tissues, organs, and structures that make up the complex human body at birth. The study of this process of the development of structure from the fertilized egg is called the science of embryology.

The study of human embryology proved to be a particularly difficult subject. The human embryo develops within the body of the mother and cannot be seen normally until the time of birth. Only those embryos that die before birth and are aborted or living embryos obtained during the course of operations can be studied by the embryologist. Knowledge of the successive steps in the long process of human development has accumulated slowly during the past century as a result of the cooperative efforts of obstetricians and embryologists. At the present time most of the processes through which the body of the human infant develops from conception to birth have been described and recorded in textbooks of human embryology.

But the general reader who wishes to learn something about human development finds that textbooks on human embryology are written in a scientific terminology that is unintelligible to anyone but a scientist. Moreover these books describe the development of each organ or system of the human body separately and in great detail, without showing how the human embryo as a whole develops month by month. This book attempts to remove these two obstacles to understanding and to present the truly fascinating tale of the development of man in intelligible terms, related in the chronological pattern of the nine calendar months that form the normal period of human development before birth.

The study of the development of the human body before birth holds for every man a fascination not often felt in the study of other fields of science. To the biologist the study of human embryology offers striking evidence of the close relation of man to other animals. To the doctor the history of the human body before birth holds the explanation for many of the peculiarities and susceptibilities of individual men that appear when the stresses of life make unusual demands on the human body. To every man the story of human development before birth presents a peculiarly intimate picture of a period in his own life that has left, to his knowledge, no imprint on his memory.

CHAPTER 1

GENESIS

LIFE BEGINS FOR EACH OF US at an unfelt, unknown, un-
honored instant when a minute, wriggling sperm plunges
headlong into a mature egg. The quiet egg, as if electrified
by the entrance of the sperm, reacts with violent agitation,
a spurt of activity, and a release of all the man-forming
potencies that are inherent in the human egg cell. It is
at this moment of fusion of the sperm and egg in fertilization that a new human being is created. From these two
cells, each of which is destined to die unless it fuses with
its mate, there arises a new human being who contains
the potentialities for unnumbered generations of men.

At this moment of fertilization there has been determined not only the existence of this human being, but
also his unique individuality. He has inherited from his
parents those hereditary traits which he in turn may transmit to his descendants. He has been endowed with a
mysterious but important quality that is aptly called viability, the ability to live, to survive the trials and adversi-
ties of life both in the uterus of his mother before birth
and in the world into which he may expect to be born
about nine months hence. The successes and the failures
of these first nine months of life, when the new human
being is changing from a nondescript, microscopic blob
of living matter into the squalling seven-pound baby that

enters the outer world at birth, form the subject of the study of human embryology.

During these first nine months of life the single fertilized egg cell will divide repeatedly to form the approximately two billion cells of the body of the infant. These developing cells will undergo a complex series of specific changes before they become the numerous organs of the human body. These organs will begin to function long before birth in the balanced, unified way that is necessary for successful living. The fertilized egg is so small that it is almost invisible unless magnified. The small quantity of living material that forms the egg will be increased about two billion times in weight during development through the growth made possible by food supplied by the mother's body. The series of events that bring about this growth and development are determined both by the genes (hereditary materials) that the embryo inherited from his parents and by the environment provided for him within his mother's body. His nature at birth and at least in part throughout his life will depend on the nature of the events and experiences that occur within him during these first nine months of life.

Before proceeding with the story of the new human being's development, it is necessary that we go back into the history of the preceding generation to observe what processes led up to this act of creation. The readily observable creators, the male and female parents, have undergone the extensive bodily changes that produce or accompany sexual maturity. This process of sexual development is too complex to be treated here, since it involves the numerous changes in the internal and external sex organs and in those endocrine glands whose secretions control sexual development and activity. The full devel-

14

opment of these sexual characters in the parents is of such importance to the new individual that it is impossible to draw a sharp line between the history of one generation and that of the next, difficult to determine at what point in time the personal history of each human being starts.

The specialized sex cells that give rise to a new individual must first undergo a peculiar process termed maturation or becoming mature. The significance of maturation of sperm and egg is appreciated only when one realizes that all human beings, of all ages or races, in all the cells of their bodies, possess forty-six discrete masses of living material called chromosomes. These are normally arranged in twenty-three pairs of chromosomes of identical size and shape. Chromosomes are the specialized parts of the living cell which contain the genes that control the nature and activities of the cell. In the egg and sperm, the chromosomes carry the physical determinants of the hereditary traits, the genes, that are transmitted from parent to offspring. The immature egg cell and sperm cell of man each contain forty-six chromosomes, and if these cells fused at fertilization the new individual would possess ninety-two chromosomes. That this does not occur has been amply proved by counts of the chromosomes in the cells of many individuals. Study of the developing egg and sperm cells show that, before they become mature and capable of fertilization, their chromosomes are reduced in number from forty-six to twenty-three.

During the final stages of maturation of the sex cells, each immature egg or sperm divides by a special process in which the two chromosomes in each pair are separated from each other and segregated into two different cells (Fig. 2). Each of these cells then contains only twenty-three chromosomes, one member of each pair of the

15

chromosomes present in the immature sex cell. Each of these new cells then divides again to form two more sex cells. Four mature sperm are thus produced from each immature sperm cell. In the egg, however, each of these two maturation divisions occurs in such a way that one large cell and one very small cell are formed. These small cells, called polar bodies, are too small to live successfully and they soon die. The single mature egg produced in each maturation division retains within itself most of the living protoplasm necessary for carrying on the activities of life. This egg protoplasm forms the first food of the developing embryo if the egg is fertilized by a sperm. When fertilization occurs, the twenty-three chromosomes of the mature sperm join with the twenty-three similar chromosomes of the mature egg to form a new human being possessing the forty-six chromosomes characteristic of man.

Two particular chromosomes are called sex chromosomes because their presence determines in part the sex of the individual. In females the two sex chromosomes are similar in size and shape, and are traditionally named the X-chromosomes. In the male the two sex chromosomes are different in size and shape, with the one that resembles the female sex chromosomes being called the X-chromosome and the other the Y-chromosome. Examination of Figure 2 will show that when the immature sperm cell undergoes maturation, these X- and Y-chromosomes are segregated from each other into separate cells. Two different types of sperm are thus produced, X bearers and Y bearers. If an X-bearing sperm fertilizes an egg, the new individual contains two X-chromosomes, one received from the father and one from the mother, and such an individual will in the normal course of development be-

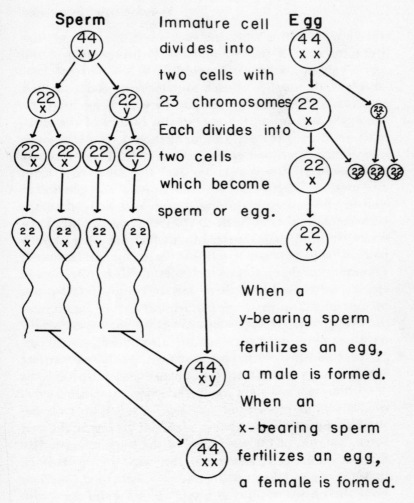

Sperm Immature cell **Egg**

divides into

two cells with

23 chromosomes

Each divides into

two cells

which become

sperm or egg.

When a

y-bearing sperm

fertilizes an egg,

a male is formed.

When an

x-bearing sperm

fertilizes an egg,

a female is formed.

FIG. 2:

Maturation of the sperm (on the left) and the egg (on the right), and their fusion in fertilization to form a male or female individual (bottom). The chromosomes carried by each sex cell are indicated by 44 (somatic chromosomes) plus X-Y (sex chromosomes) in the male, and 44 plus X-X in the female.

come a female. If a Y-bearing sperm fertilizes the egg, the X-chromosome of the egg and the Y-chromosome of the sperm pair up to form the typical male X-Y pattern.

The individuality of each human being is determined in part at the time of fertilization by what genes are present in the sperm and the egg, so this history of the chromosomes during the maturation of the sex cells is of great importance. Each one of us receives half of our forty-six chromosomes from our father and the other half from our mother. These chromosomes contain the genes that control the processes through which our body develops both before and after birth. During the maturation of the sex cells, blind chance determines which member of each pair of chromosomes goes into each mature sex cell. Chance again determines which sperm will fertilize which egg. It is believed that there are well over 15,000 genes present in a human chromosome, and chance determines the exact nature of each gene. Yet these chance events determine not only our sex, but also our physical, physiological, and possibly psychological nature. So the moment of fertilization, when all of these chance events converge to determine the inherited nature of a new human being, is truly a unique moment of creation.

The journey of a sperm in search of an egg might well be the caption of the next stage of the human story. The mature sperm cell, formed in the testis of the mature male, is the smallest but most motile cell of the human body. It consists of an oval head, which carries the sperm chromosomes, and a long, slender, filamentous tail that can vibrate back and forth to produce fairly rapid motion of the minute sperm (Fig. 1). The sperm must travel over a long, tortuous, hazardous course before it can accomplish its sole purpose in life, fusion with an egg.

Millions of sperm fail for each one that succeeds. In this journey the sperm must travel over a distance of more than twenty feet through the coiled sex ducts of the male before they can be ejaculated from the penis (Fig. 3). Through the lashing of their threadlike tails, the sperm are able to swim forward at the rate of approximately one inch in twenty minutes. When they are injected into the vagina of a female, rhythmic muscular contractions of the female sex ducts help propel the sperm up through the uterus and the Fallopian tubes. If a mature egg has been released from the ovary, the sperm may meet and fertilize the egg in the upper end of the tube.

Time is an important element in this arduous journey of the sperm. The sperm leaves the testis with a certain amount of energy for swimming and for fertilizing, and it is essential that it reach and enter the egg before it loses this energy. Studies of fertility in man suggest that only a relatively small number of the several million sperm that are ejaculated at one time succeed in traveling the full length of the female sex ducts and thus winning the opportunity to fertilize an egg. It is not known exactly how long it takes the sperm to make its journey, but it seems likely that the sperm reaches the upper end of the female sex ducts within a few hours at most. Nor is it known how long the sperm can wait there for the egg without losing too much of its precious energy, but it seems probable that the passage of several more hours will make the sperm incapable of entering the egg.

Sperm are formed and matured more or less continuously in the mature male, but a mature egg is formed only once each month in the mature female. The egg grows and matures slowly within the ovary and is released from the ovary at one particular stage in the continuous,

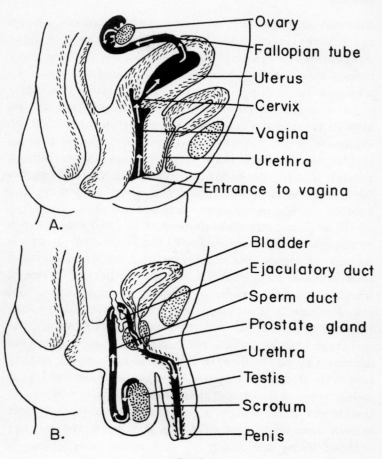

- Ovary
- Fallopian tube
- Uterus
- Cervix
- Vagina
- Urethra
- Entrance to vagina

A.

- Bladder
- Ejaculatory duct
- Sperm duct
- Prostate gland
- Urethra
- Testis
- Scrotum
- Penis

B.

FIG. 3:

The female reproductive organs (A) and the male reproductive organs (B) with the cavities of the passages shown in solid black. The path followed by the sperm from the testis, through the sperm duct, and out the urethra of the penis is shown by arrows in B. The path taken by the sperm through the vagina, uterus, and Fallopian tubes in the female is similarly shown by arrows in A. The egg is released from the ovary and passes into the upper end of the Fallopian tube where it may be met and fertilized by a sperm.

20

rhythmic female sexual cycle. This release of the mature egg, a process called ovulation, occurs once in each menstrual cycle of the sexually mature female, usually at some time about halfway between two successive menstruations.

The egg falls, or is moved in a fashion not clearly understood, into the open funnel-shaped end of the Fallopian tube. Within the tube it starts on its journey of life, which differs from that of the sperm in being shorter, slower, less hazardous, and probably requiring no energy of the egg itself. It moves slowly down the Fallopian tube and into the uterus, traversing a distance of about four inches in approximately four days. If it is met and entered by a sperm, it at once embarks on the process of becoming a human being. If it misses this rendezvous for which it was created, nurtured, and matured, it languishes a short time within the uterus, dies a degenerate death, and is probably expelled from the body.

These unused eggs and the millions of superfluous sperm that die without fulfilling their purpose in life represent mankind's margin of safety, the excess of sexual cells produced to insure an adequate supply of offspring to maintain the population of our species in spite of the hazards that threaten all developing animals. The fertility of each species determines in part the success of that species in the struggle for survival. In biological terms, successful reproduction is the primary purpose of life for each adult animal.

In man the first step in reproduction is achieved when a fully mature sperm fertilizes a fully mature egg. The exact day when this occurs in individual cases is difficult to determine. The human egg matures and is released from the ovary near the middle of the period between two menstruations in the woman. In individual women this time of ovulation may vary from the eighth to the twentieth day of the menstrual cycle, although in the majority of women ovulation occurs near the end of the second week after the beginning of menstruation. The egg must be fertilized fairly promptly or it becomes incapable of normal development. This means that each new human being begins his life on a day that occurs about two weeks after the last menstrual period of his mother before pregnancy. The personal age of each human being during his prenatal life is therefore about two weeks less than the length of time that has passed since the beginning of the last menstruation before pregnancy. Human pregnancy lasts about forty weeks, counting from the beginning of the last menstruation to the time of delivery of the infant, and the infant is about thirty-eight weeks old at the time of birth. In this book the age of the developing individual is measured from the true beginning of his life, the moment of fertilization.

But the fertilized egg is only potentially a new human being. It must undergo a long and complex series of developmental changes before it can live independently. During this first stage of human life we live parasitically within the uterus of our mother, whose body provides the food, warmth, and protection necessary for our survival. In this way the generations of men overlap in time, with one generation not only creating but nurturing the next generation. The biography of the unborn human is a part of the biography of his parents.

CHAPTER 2

THE FIRST MONTH:

OUT OF THE UNKNOWN

OUT OF THE UNKNOWN into the image of Man—this is the miraculous change that occurs during the first month of human life. We grow from an egg cell so small as to be barely visible (about 1/200 of an inch wide) to a young human embryo one fifth of an inch long, increasing fifty times in size and 40,000 times in weight. We change from a small round egg cell into a creature with a head, a body, and it must be admitted, a tail; with a heart that beats and blood that circulates; with the beginnings of arms and legs, eyes and ears, stomach and brain. In fact during the first four weeks of our life almost every organ that serves us throughout our entire life has started to form. In addition to this astounding growth and development, during this first month we must make our first struggle for food. For this purpose we develop a special organ, the placenta, which enables us to draw food from our mother, allowing us to live a life of ease within the tissues of her uterus.

The human egg, after it has been fertilized by a sperm, continues to travel down the uterine tube toward the uterus (Fig. 4). During this journey, which takes about five days, the egg starts to develop. Shortly after fertiliza-

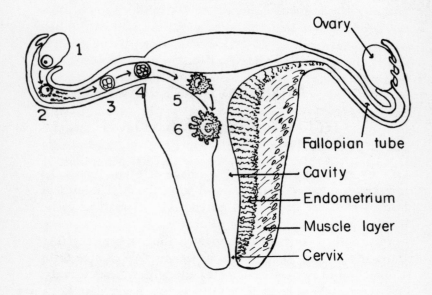

FIG. 4:

The uterus, Fallopian tubes, and ovaries of the mature woman. On the left side is shown the sequence of events that occurs during the first week of human pregnancy. The egg is released from the ovary (1) into the upper end of the Fallopian tube, where it is met and fertilized by the sperm (2). The fertilized egg divides repeatedly as it passes slowly down the Fallopian tube (3) until it forms a solid ball of cells, the morula (4). The egg enters the cavity of the uterus on about the fifth or sixth day after fertilization, when it has the form of a hollow vesicle, a blastocyst (5). On about the seventh day the developing egg begins to invade the endometrial lining of the uterus (6). The embryo is completely implanted within the wall of the uterus by the end of the second week of life.

24

tion the activity that was stirred up in the egg by the entrance of the sperm leads to the division of the egg into two cells that are believed to be identical with each other in form and content. A meticulously exact living process called mitosis, which brings about the division of one living cell into two cells, serves to distribute all of the materials present within the egg equally between the two daughter cells. This equal division of the material bases of life occurs particularly in the division of the chromosomes. These first two cells may rarely become completely separated from each other in some unknown manner. If this occurs each cell will continue to develop, and these two cells will form two complete individuals who thereby become identical twins. Nonidentical or fraternal twins may be formed when two eggs are ovulated at about the same time, fertilized by separate sperm, and both successfully embed in the uterus and undergo development.

The first two cells in turn divide by mitosis into four cells, the four divide into eight, the eight into sixteen, the sixteen into thirty-two, on and on until the time of death. This process of the division of the fertilized egg into many cells is called cleavage, and it is the process by which all animals begin their development. Such cell division is of great importance not only because it leads to the formation of the millions of cells that form the human body, but because it allows the body to grow in size, and makes possible the differentiation of the many different kinds of cells that compose the various organs of the body. During development each separate cell undergoes a gradual process of successive changes that make it different from all other cells, until finally it becomes a mature, specialized cell, performing one particular function for the living organism. Some of the embryonic cells thus

25

formed serve their purpose in the life of the embryo and then die; other cells become part of the growing body of the infant. All of the cells that form the body of the infant, the child, and the adult are direct lineal descendants by mitosis from the original fertilized egg cell.

By the fifth day after fertilization, the human egg has divided into almost one hundred cells, forming a small ball called a morula. Within this solid ball of cells the second step of development now occurs. A small cavity forms in the center of the morula, converting it into a hollow ball of cells called a blastocyst. At this time the developing human egg enters the cavity of the uterus (Fig. 4). There the egg, which is believed to be sticky on the surface, adheres to the special lining of the uterus, the endometrium. The spot where the egg attaches to the wall of the uterus is apparently a matter of chance, since different human embryos have been found to be developing in various locations. By the seventh day the cells that lie on the surface of the developing egg begin to force their way into the endometrium, burying the egg within the tissues of the uterus. By the end of the second week of life the human egg has become completely embedded within the tissues of its mother's uterus, in the place where it will live until birth occurs. From this time on, the food materials supplied by the mother will make rapid growth and development possible.

Not all developing animal eggs are as fortunate as are the eggs of man and other mammals. In most animals the egg leaves the body of the mother either before or soon after it is fertilized and then undergoes its development without the benefit of a maternal supply of food, warmth, and protection. Only in mammals, except for a few special cases in some fish and reptiles, does the devel-

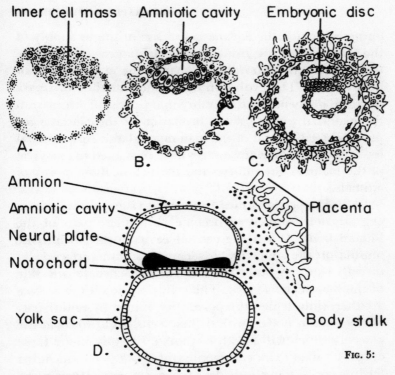

Inner cell mass   Amniotic cavity   Embryonic disc

A.

B.

C.

Amnion
Amniotic cavity
Neural plate
Notochord

Placenta

Yolk sac

Body stalk

D.

Fig. 5:

Diagrams showing the development of the human embryo during the
second and third weeks after fertilization. The ages given for each stage
are approximate and may vary in individual cases.

A. Six days. The blastocyst is formed of an outer layer of trophoblast
cells and an excentric inner cell mass.

B. Eight days. The trophoblast cells project from all sides of the blastocyst. The inner cell mass becomes split by a cavity, the amniotic cavity,
into an outer layer of cells (the future amniotic sac) and the inner
embryonic disc.

C. Fourteen days. The trophoblast cells form diffuse villi around the
blastocyst. The embryonic disc becomes a flattened plate overlain by the
amniotic cavity and sac. A hollow bag, the yolk sac, forms below the
embryonic disc.

D. A diagrammatic longitudinal section through the embryonic disc,
body stalk, and part of the trophoblast on about the sixteenth day. The
future head end of the embryo lies at the left side of the diagram, the
tail end at the right. The embryonic disc has formed the neural plate and
the notochord. The embryo is attached to the placenta through the body
stalk, the future umbilical cord.

(Based on Patten.)

27

oping egg enjoy the advantages of a continuous supply of the food needed for growth and development, and of protection from the hazards of a changeable environment or of predators. The evolution of this new method of reproduction, of spending the embryonic period of life within the maternal uterus, of the formation of the placenta for prenatal feeding and of the mammary glands for postnatal feeding—all of these advantages have promoted the survival of the mammalian embryo and the mammalian species of animals.

All of the cells formed from the division of the human egg are not destined to become permanent parts of the human body. When the central cavity forms within the morula on the sixth day, it separates a thin surface layer of cells from an inner mass of cells attached to one side of the blastocyst (Fig. 5). The cells that lie on the surface are therewith denied the possibility of ever becoming part of the human body. Instead these cells begin to form the placenta which will feed the embryo. For this reason these cells are called extra-embryonic trophoblast cells, meaning feeding cells lying outside of the embryo. During the second week of human development, the trophoblast cells grow rapidly until they form a velvety covering of branching, finger-like processes all over the surface of the blastocyst. These tentacles of growing cells invade, destroy, and engulf the tissues of the uterus, using the materials obtained from the destroyed uterine cells as food for their own growth and the growth of all the other embryonic cells.

Now it must be admitted that the mother's tissues do not tolerate this destructive action by the embryonic trophoblast without a protest. When the fertilized egg reaches the uterus, the tissues lining the uterus are in a very active

28

state, rich in blood, glands prepared for secretion, everything ripe and ready for the coming egg much as a well-plowed and fertilized field is ready for seed. This fortunate preparedness does not result from any knowledge that the egg has been fertilized and will soon embed. The same process occurs each month when an egg is released from the ovary. Hormones secreted by the ovary and the pituitary gland act in concert to prepare the uterus for possible pregnancy once each month during the sexual maturity of a woman. If the egg is fertilized, it finds the uterus ready for it when it reaches the uterus six days later. If fertilization does not occur, the uterus loses its excess tissue and blood in the menstrual flow, and starts on a new period of repair and growth, on the principle of better luck next time.

When the egg burrows its way into the uterine lining, the surrounding maternal tissues react at first as if to an enemy. Cells that serve as protectors of the body against foreign invasion are rushed to the spot, somewhat as if the egg were an infection. More blood is forced through the uterine blood vessels, the glands secrete actively, and the maternal tissues surrounding the egg grow and enlarge. As the trophoblast scavengers destroy more and more maternal tissues, the blood vessels of the uterus are eroded open and a pool of maternal blood forms around the developing egg. From this pool the trophoblast cells begin to absorb food, water, and oxygen needed by the growing embryo. The mother's tissues resign themselves to the presence of this destructive invader, form a protective wall of tougher tissues around the invaded region, and within this area cooperate with the trophoblast in forming an efficient organ for feeding the growing embryo, the placenta.

How does the mother's body know that an egg has been fertilized and is embedding in the uterus? Why does the next menstruation usually not occur? For a long time these questions were unanswerable, and the mother herself knew that she was pregnant only after two menstrual periods had been missed. But in the past fifty years study of the hormones that act as biological informers and controllers in the human body has led to a better understanding of the role of hormones in pregnancy. The growing trophoblast cells of the embryo secrete special hormones, called placental hormones, into the maternal blood that surrounds them in the uterus. These hormones then circulate in the blood stream throughout the mother's body, and provoke the necessary reactions of the ovary, uterus, and pituitary gland to suppress further menstruation and to promote the adjustment of the mother's body to the demands of pregnancy. Such large amounts of these pregnancy hormones are secreted into the mother's blood that the excess hormones are excreted into her urine. If these placental hormones are then separated from a sample of the urine and injected into an immature female mouse or other animal, they provoke typical reactions of the ovaries and uterus of the test animal. Through this test it is possible to determine whether or not a woman is pregnant within three or four weeks after fertilization, or five to seven weeks after her last menstruation.

The placenta is a special temporary organ formed anew in each pregnancy and discarded at the birth of the infant. It is created by the growing trophoblast cells of the embryo and the maternal tissues of the uterus that the trophoblast invades. Both the maternal and the embryonic parts of the placenta are necessary for the successful development of the human embryo. The blood and the tissues of the mother bring to the placenta the materials that make possible the growth and development of the embryo. The embryonic tissues of the placenta absorb these materials from the mother's blood, synthesize them into the kinds of chemicals needed by the embryo, and pass these new materials on to the developing embryo. The very young embryo is connected to the placenta by a special extra-embryonic structure, the body stalk (Fig. 5 D). During the fourth week of life the human embryo develops a beating heart, blood, and blood vessels that carry the embryonic blood throughout the embryo's body, out to the placenta, and back to the embryo. Within the placenta the embryonic blood picks up the nutritive materials absorbed by the trophoblast from the mother's blood and carries them to the growing embryo. Waste products formed within the embryonic body are carried out to the placenta and there passed over to the mother's blood, which then disposes of these wastes through the mother's kidney and lungs. Within the placenta the two blood streams, the mother's and the embryo's, flow slowly past each other, separated by the trophoblast cells. In no case does the mother's blood circulate through the body of the embryo, a prevalent but quite unfounded belief.

The placenta forms the functional connecting link between the mother and her child during the first nine months of its life, and the way in which it functions determines the success or failure of prenatal development. Out of the materials, the energies, and the hereditary traits with which the new individual was endowed at conception, there can develop only such structures as the placenta adequately nourishes and protects. Although the humanity of the new individual was insured in the egg and sperm, his perfections or imperfections depend largely on the efficiency of the placenta. The human embryo is not an intimate part of the mother's body, but a stranger temporarily housed within the uterus. The embryo has a different hereditary nature from the mother, since it is created and controlled by genes from the father as much as from the mother, and sometimes these two hereditary natures conflict with each other. Because the developing embryo is undergoing an intricate process of change, it has different needs from those of the fully developed mother, so some substances that may be useful to the mother may be harmful to the embryo. In the placenta these differences and conflicts meet in the trophoblast cells that determine which materials are permitted to pass from mother to embryo and from embryo to mother. Biologists speak almost reverently of the placental barrier, some unknown force that controls this exchange between mother and child. The first battles of our life are fought at this placental barrier.

During the second and third weeks of life the next stage of development occurs as the blastocyst becomes an embryo. Within the inner cell mass the future amniotic cavity and the yolk sac cavity form, leaving a thickened plate of cells lying between these two cavities. This is the embryonic disc, and only these cells will become a permanent part of the developing embryo. Considering what a small number of cells there is in the developing human egg, it is surprising to find it immediately setting aside one group of cells after another for structures that will be discarded at birth, leaving only a very small fraction of the original cell mass to carry out the complex task of forming the entire human body.

All of these temporary structures are called extra-embryonic membranes, and it is their job to feed and

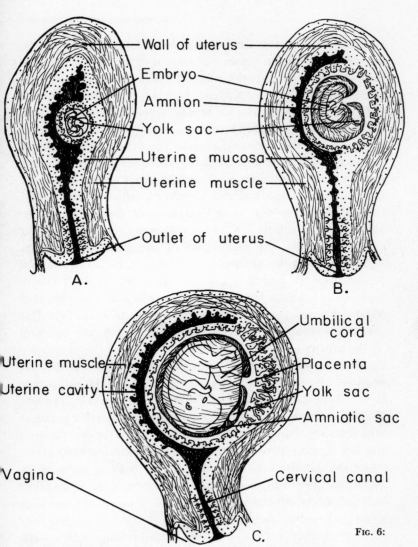

Wall of uterus

Embryo

Amnion

Yolk sac

Uterine mucosa

Uterine muscle

Outlet of uterus

A.

B.

Umbilical cord

Uterine muscle

Uterine cavity

Placenta

Yolk sac

Amniotic sac

Vagina

Cervical canal

C.

Fig. 6:

Diagrams showing the pregnant uterus during the first two months of pregnancy, with the embryo and the embryonic membranes in the proper relative size and position within the wall of the uterus. (Based on Patten.)

A. At three weeks of development.
B. At five weeks of development.
C. At eight weeks of development.

C. At eight weeks of development.

protect the embryo during the formative period of life. There are four of these extra-embryonic membranes in human development (Fig. 6). (1) The trophoblast forms the embryonic part of the placenta. (2) The thin transparent amniotic sac surrounds the growing embryo until birth. Its cavity is filled with a watery fluid that steadily increases in amount, surrounding the fragile embryo with a water-jacket that acts as shock absorber, deadening any jolts or blows that may strike the mother's body, preventing injury to the soft, delicate embryo. At birth the amniotic sac ruptures and the fluid escapes from the uterus ahead of the infant. (3) The yolk sac forms a small sac suspended from the belly side of the embryo. This sac is called the yolk sac because it is similar in form and position to the sac that contains yolk in the embryos of reptiles and birds. In man it never contains any yolk and has no known function in feeding the embryo. (4) The allantois is a small, vestigial outgrowth from the tail end of the embryo.

As the embryo grows, the placenta invades more and more of the wall of the uterus, until it covers about one third of the inner surface of the expanding uterus. During the first four months of development the placenta is larger and heavier than the embryo which it feeds, but during the last five months of intra-uterine life the embryo grows more rapidly than the placenta. At birth all of these extra-embryonic membranes, their usefulness ended, are left behind in the uterus when the child is born and are then discarded as the after-birth.

The presence of a yolk sac without any yolk in the young human embryo is but one illustration of a puzzling aspect of human development. During the first two months of its life the human embryo develops several structures

34

that are of no known use to the human embryo, that never become a functional part of the human body. In each case the unused, discarded structure is almost identical with a similar structure that is a necessary part of the embryo in other animals less complex than man. Moreover, during the first four weeks of human development, the human embryo undergoes a series of developmental steps that are nearly identical with the first steps taken in the embryonic development of such diverse animals as a fish, a salamander, a snake, a chicken, a pig, a horse, or a monkey. When this amazing similarity between embryos was first discovered, it was interpreted as showing the common evolutionary origin of all animals from the same ancestors in the distant past. The embryos of all animals were believed to retrace the course of evolution in their development, resembling at successive times an ancestral fish form, then progressing 'up' the evolutionary ladder through successive stages of evolution until finally the embryo reaches the level of organization that characterizes its particular species of animal. Human development was believed to repeat in brief the course of human evolution, developing structures like the yolk sac that had been useful to other forms of animals but were of no use to the human embryo. But even in these early stages there are many specific traits that identify the young embryo as being unquestionably human. The human embryo in its development is always controlled by its specifically human genes, and at no time is it anything but a distinctly human creature in spite of its superficial resemblance to the embryos of other animals.

The truly permanent part of the developing embryo begins the process of becoming a human being during the third and fourth weeks of the first month of life. The few cells that form the embryonic disc at the end of the second week are more or less unspecialized, so that any cell is probably able to form any part of the future body. Step by step, one small change produces another change, this produces several more changes, on and on this sequence goes, with each change marking out different cells for different fates until the typical human body is formed. Even after birth the sequence of change continues throughout childhood, adolescence, maturity, old age and death. The whole sequence is started in the developing egg, but the future man is no more present in the egg than the oak tree is present within the acorn.

The first human structures to develop are the precursors of the brain and the heart. During the third week the cells of the embryonic disc thicken to form an oval plate of cells called the neural plate (Fig. 7). The immediate cause of this beginning of the future nervous system is the differentiation of a median cord of cells, the notochord, which in some unknown way induces the embryonic cells overlying it to specialize as future nerve cells. The neural plate continues to thicken during the third week and the edges of the plate roll upward to form two parallel ridges, the neural folds. These neural folds bend upward and toward each other over the surface of the neural plate, meet in the midline of the future embryonic body, and begin to fuse with each other, converting the flat neural plate into a closed tube. This neural tube is the precursor of the highly elaborate nervous system, the beginning of the brain that is man's most precious bodily possession.

The rapidity of this first truly embryonic development is amazing. In only five days the flat, undifferentiated embryonic disc has become a definitely structured embryo

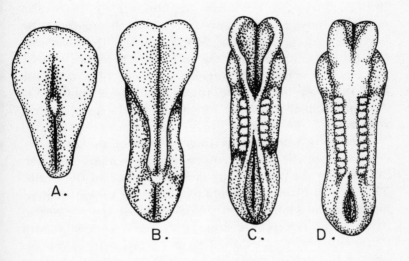

Fig. 7:

Surface views of the human embryonic disc during the early development of the nervous system. (Based on Arey.)

A. 18 days. The flat, oval embryonic disc thickens to form the neural plate.

B. 20 days. The edges of the neural plate bulge upwards to form two neural folds.

C. 22 days. The neural folds begin to fuse with each other near the middle of the neural plate. Six pairs of somites have formed along either side of the closing neural tube.

D. 23 days. The neural folds have fused completely except near the two ends of the elongating embryo, forming a closed neural tube. Ten pairs of somites have formed.

with the planes of symmetry of the future body established in head and tail ends, right and left sides. The wide end of the closing neural tube marks the head end of the future embryo and the narrowing opposite end marks the tail end. Between these two extremities the neural tube begins to differentiate into future brain at the head end and future spinal cord at the tail end. On either side of the closing neural tube successive blocks of a different kind of tissue are formed internally. These somites, as they are called, form the precursors of the muscles and vertebrae of the embryo.

One may wonder how these details of the early development of the human embryo are known and how one can say that the neural plate is the precursor of the brain. The facts of human development that are presented here have become known slowly, as a result of the systematic study of uteri removed from numerous women during therapeutic operations or of tissues scraped from the inside of the uterus. Occasionally such examinations show the presence of a very young human embryo embedded in the uterine wall. Such embryos are then studied carefully and in detail, and the facts gained are correlated with other bits of knowledge gained from other similar studies. Embryologists then compare and correlate the details of human development with the better known details of the development of other animals that can be studied while they are alive. In this way we have arrived at a fairly thorough knowledge of the consecutive stages in the development of the human embryo. Later stages of human development have been studied in embryos or fetuses that are lost through miscarriage or death. Although our knowledge of the facts of human development thus depends on tragic loss of human lives, we use this knowledge to improve the lives of other more fortunate human beings through our understanding of the course and problems of human development.

The human heart also undergoes precocious, rapid development during the third week of life. On the sixteenth day the first definitely specialized cells appear as young blood cells, formed in the walls of the yolk sac in clusters called blood islands. These blood islands grow and differentiate into a fine network of blood vessels, thin walled tubes in which fluid and free blood cells float. In succeeding days more blood islands form, differentiate, and their vessels grow into the embryonic disc in the form of two symmetrical tubes, the prospective heart tubes. By the twenty-second day these two simple tubes have fused with each other under the developing neural plate to form a single heart tube.

This simple heart tube must undergo numerous changes and many days of growth before it becomes the typical human heart, but rather than wait for that distant day before starting to work, the heart tube begins pulsating at once. Cells in the walls of the heart tube differentiate into the first muscle cells of the human body and begin to contract. First a slight twitch runs through the heart tube, then another and another, and soon the heart is rhythmically expanding and contracting. The free blood cells and the fluid forming in the blood islands are drawn into the heart tube, propelled forward jerkily at each pulsation of the heart, and forced out through the small blood vessels that have formed in the embryonic disc. The embryonic heart begins to beat on about the twenty-fourth day of life, and for the remaining eight months of prenatal life and sixty or more years of independent life of the individual, the heart must continue to beat. Once the heart starts beating on the twenty-fourth day after fertilization, the life of the individual depends on the continuous, steady, rhythmic beating of the heart. Biologists of earlier times, in studying young embryos of various animals, were so impressed with the miracle of the tiny heart beating in the otherwise simple embryo that they believed that this was the moment when the vital spark of life entered the body.

This rapid development of the neural tube and heart, of organization and symmetry out of the simplicity of the embryonic disc in the space of only seven days, reflects the value to the embryo of the precocious development of the placenta. Once the trophoblast has established functional relations with the sources of food materials within the mother's uterus, the truly embryonic part of the human egg immediately enters a period of explosive growth and miraculously complex change. During the third and fourth weeks of our life we undergo more rapid and complex changes than at any other period of our entire life span.

This is a critical stage in the life of the individual, a time when any small disturbance of the normal sequence of developmental events can produce an effect that will be magnified progressively as growth and development proceed. Studies of the causes of abnormal development, of the numerous defects that can occur in the human body during its development, have shown that the third and fourth weeks of prenatal life are probably the most sensitive period in human development. When we recall that this period in the life of the embryo occurs during the time when the mother does not yet know that she is pregnant, and that the mother's body provides the environment in which the sensitive embryo is living, we realize the importance of events in the mother's life that might affect the environment of the unknown embryo within her uterus. Variations in the diet of the mother, in the drugs she takes into her body, in the illnesses she may experience, all may affect the embryo. During this critical period in its life such events in the mother's life may have far more important effects on the embryo than they would at a later period. Just as a mark on a deflated balloon will enlarge progressively as the balloon expands, so a small aberration occurring early in embryonic life may lead to extensive defects in the process of growth and development. For this reason women have a special responsibility for guarding their health during the period of their lives when they might become pregnant.

During the fourth week of life the human embryo grows rapidly, tripling its size in seven days (Fig. 8). At the beginning of this week the external form of the embryo is relatively simple and distinctly nonhuman. The twenty-four-day-old embryo has the form of a straight tube about one tenth of an inch long. The head consists solely of the brain and primitive eye. The heart forms a prominent bulge on the belly side of the embryo. Immediately behind the heart the wide umbilical cord attaches the embryo to the placenta. Along the back, thirteen somites, formed along either side of the spinal cord, mold the thin skin into a succession of small bumps.

During the remainder of the fourth week, the shape of the embryo changes as the body curves into an almost closed circle, with the tail nearly touching the head. The brain and heart grow rapidly, forming increasingly prominent bulges of the body wall. Behind the head on either side of the future neck a series of three grooves and ridges appears. These are external evidence of one of the most

41

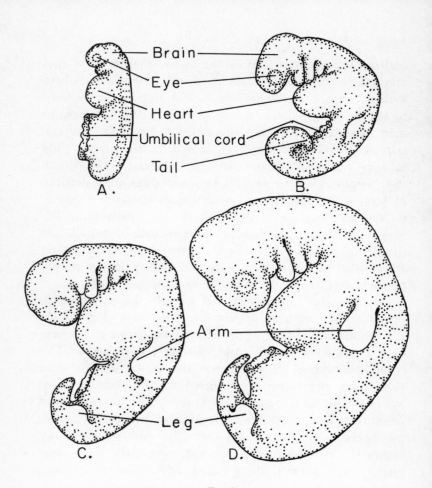

FIG. 8:

Development of the human embryo during the fourth week of life. Each embryo is drawn ten times its actual size, and is shown from its left side. The umbilical cord has been cut off near the belly of the embryo. The drawings are based on photographs of embryos described by Streeter.
A. Twenty-four days.
B. Twenty-six days.
C. Twenty-eight days.
D. Thirty days.

42

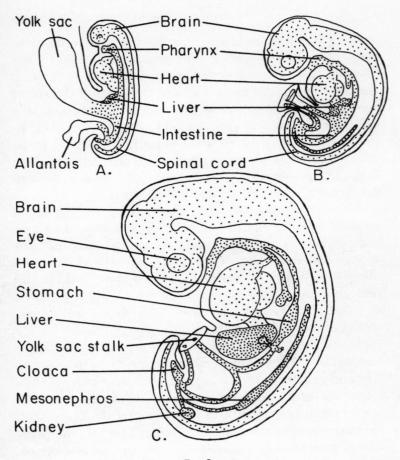

Yolk sac
Brain
Pharynx
Heart
Liver
Intestine
Allantois
Spinal cord
A.
B.

Brain
Eye
Heart
Stomach
Liver
Yolk sac stalk
Cloaca
Mesonephros
Kidney
C.

FIG. 9:

Development of the internal organs of the human embryo during the fourth week. Each embryo is outlined in profile from the left side and the internal organs are shown in their proper places within the embryonic body. The three embryos are drawn to the same magnification (ten times actual size), so comparison of the three diagrams shows the great growth that occurs in the brain and heart. (Based on Streeter.)
A. Twenty-four days; same embryo pictured in Fig. 8 A.
B. Twenty-six days: same embryo pictured in Fig. 8 B.
C. Thirty days; same embryo pictured in Fig. 8 D.

43

puzzling illustrations of the repetition in human development of structures useful only to other animals, in this case the fish. These grooves are comparable in position and development to the gill slits of the fish and the ridges between the grooves are similar to the gill bars in the fish neck. In the fish, gill slits and gills develop here. In the human embryo these grooves do not normally break through into the throat cavity nor do gills develop. The ridges are remodelled during the second month to form the face and neck of the human embryo.

On the sides of the body two sets of paddle-shaped bulges form the precursors of arms and legs. The arm buds appear on the twenty-sixth day and similar leg buds appear two days later. These four nubbins of skin and internal cells bear no resemblance to human limbs at this time, but during the next month arms and legs, hands and feet, fingers and toes will differentiate from these unprepossessing limb buds.

Within this unhuman exterior nearly all of the organs that make up the human body begin to form (Fig. 9). The originally flat, double-layered embryonic disc is rolled up into a double-walled tube, with the outermost layer forming the skin of the embryo and the inner layer forming the digestive tract. In the head region, the primitive digestive tract expands to form the wide pharynx, which will become part of the mouth and throat cavities. From the middle of the digestive tract the vestigial yolk sac is suspended. From the hind end of the digestive tract a second vestigial sac, the allantois, is outpocketed. The allantois is another extra-embryonic membrane, similar in form and position to a much larger sac that has an important function in the developing bird egg. Within two days the connections of both the yolk sac and the allantois with the embryonic digestive tract have narrowed to very slender stalks, the former attached to the intestine and the latter to the future urinary bladder. From the floor of the intestine in front of the yolk stalk an outgrowth of cells forms the beginning of the liver, an organ that grows very rapidly to fill the entire abdominal cavity below the enlarging heart. By the end of the fourth week the digestive tract has begun to differentiate into a mouth cavity, a wide pharynx, a narrow esophagus leading to the expanding stomach, and a slender tubular intestine ending in a widened chamber called the cloaca (the appropriate technical term for a sewer). From the floor of the pharynx a single median lung bud forms on the twenty-sixth day, and grows rapidly in length behind the heart to form the future trachea and the buds of two lungs.

Near the end of the fourth week the human embryo begins on a long and devious path that will ultimately lead to the formation of his kidneys. The development of the human kidney presents another striking example of the recapitulation during development of evolutionary history. Instead of forming directly the type of kidney that the human animal has, the embryo first develops a much simpler type of kidney. This primitive fish-type kidney, called a pronephros, appears as a series of small tubules in the future neck region of the embryonic body. But these tubules are poorly developed and soon degenerate, as if the human embryo were merely tentatively recalling an earlier experiment in kidney formation. Before the end of the fourth week a second attempt at kidney formation starts, this time more sustained and resulting in the formation of a long, slender organ, the middle kidney or mesonephros, lying along the back between the

45

intestine and spinal cord. This kidney develops farther than did the pronephros, becoming differentiated into numerous coiled tubules that may secrete urine for a short time during the second month of life. During the second month of life the mesonephros will be converted into ducts of the male reproductive system. But the human embryo, as if its human genes intimated that even this would not be an adequate human kidney, begins the development of still a third type of kidney, the meta-nephros. This final kidney begins at the end of the first month as a small round outpocketing from the duct of the mesonephros near the tail end of the body.

Scientists interpret this strange process of forming three successive types of kidney as being a hasty, sketchy repetition in the human embryo of the long, tortuous process of evolution. It is as if every time a modern machine were built the builder first made the oldest, simplest machine of that kind ever made, took this primitive machine apart and out of the old and some new parts built a succession of more modern machines, finally building a truly new model.

So the human embryo completes the first month of life. After a slow first week of cell division and traveling to the uterus, the egg established itself within the wall of the mother's uterus where a rich supply of food was made available through the developing placenta. During the third week the basic preliminary tissues of the embryo were formed. Once this was completed, a great burst of activity and growth swept through the embryo, and within little more than one week the foundations for almost all of the organs of the human body were laid down. In thirty days the new human being has traveled the path from the mysteriously simple egg and sperm to the threshold of humanity.

CHAPTER 3

THE SECOND MONTH:
THE FACE OF MAN

FROM TADPOLE TO MAN: so one might characterize the changes that occur during the second month of human development. True, the embryo is not a tadpole at the beginning of the month, but it looks not unlike one (Fig. 10). This tailed, bulbous creature, with its enormous drooping head, fish-like gill clefts, and formless stubs for arms and legs bears little resemblance to an acceptable human form. By the end of the second month, however, the embryo has a distinctly human appearance and would be recognized by anyone as a promising example of *Homo sapiens*. He possesses an unmistakable although rather grotesque human face; a smooth neck proudly supporting his still large head; arms and legs possessing elbows and knees, fingers and toes; an elongated trunk whose smoothly rounded belly and muscular back no longer show the contours of the organs within. The human tail, another reminder of our relationship with other animals, reaches its maximum length during this month and then regresses as it is hidden by the growing buttocks. The rapid growth that started during the fourth week continues and the embryo grows five times in length and fifty times in weight, until at the end of the second month he is a clearly visible creature about one inch in length and one gram in weight.

During the second month the internal organs of the embryo develop rapidly. In fact the liver, stomach, and intestines grow so rapidly that they crowd each other too much within the small belly cavity, and the long, coiled intestine is shoved partially out of the body through the gap in the belly wall where the umbilical cord is attached to the embryo (Fig. 10 D). This swollen bag of intestines, which detracts so much from the appearance of the human embryo at the end of the second month, is called a normal umbilical hernia. Fortunately it will disappear as the size of the belly grows, and by the fourth month the intestines will be drawn back inside of the embryo's body.

But the main feature that makes the two-month-old embryo begin to resemble a human being is the development of the human face (Fig. 11). At the beginning of the second month the head of the embryo consists almost entirely of the expanding bulbous brain, whose contours mold the thin skin of the head. Below the brain the growing eyes bulge out from opposite sides of the head. Shallow pits of specialized skin, the future olfactory tissues of the nose, overlie the front end of the brain. Between the overhanging brain and the bulging chest lies a wide, gaping hole, the mouth. At either side of the mouth a series of grooves and ridges still mark the human embryo as being related to its fish-like ancestors.

The human face is built up gradually around the wide mouth, the bulging eyes, the sinking nasal pits, and the useless 'gill' bars and grooves. The first step is the formation of a lower jaw on the floor of the mouth cavity. During the fifth week the first pair of ridges on the sides

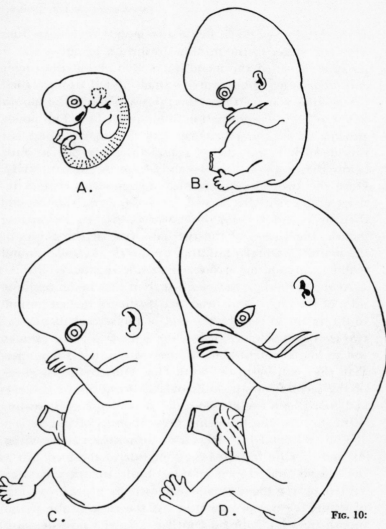

Fig. 10:

Development of the human embryo during the second month of life. Each embryo is drawn two and one half times its actual size, and is shown from its left side (25 mm. equal one inch). The umbilical cord is cut off near the belly of the embryo. The drawings are based on photographs of embryos described by Streeter.

A. Fifth week. Actual size 10 mm.   C. Seventh week. Actual size 30 mm.
B. Sixth week. Actual size 20 mm.   D. Eighth week. Actual size 37 mm.

of the head grow down below the mouth cavity and fuse with each other in the midline to form a primitive lower jaw that is called the mandibular arch. From the upper ends of each mandibular arch a small bud of tissue (called the maxillary arch) then grows forward above the mouth cavity to begin the formation of an upper jaw. The slowly growing maxillary arches fuse with the sides of the nasal pits in such a way that a complete upper jaw is built below the eyes and nostrils, and above the mouth cavity. Once the two jaws are formed, the mouth becomes restricted to a slit that is still far wider from side to side than is customary for human mouths. In succeeding months the tissues of the two jaws fuse at the angles of the mouth, gradually building up the cheeks and lips and making the mouth narrower from side to side.

At the same time the eyes, which at first lie on opposite sides of the embryonic head, are gradually moved around to the front, so that by the end of the second month the two eyes gaze at more or less the same field. But even in the newborn infant the two eyes are still farther apart than they will be in the adult face. During the last week of the second month, folds of skin form above the eyes and soon these eyelids close down over the eyes, sealing them shut for the following three months of life.

The two nasal pits deepen to form true nasal cavities. At first they lie far out on either side of the face, but as the cheeks and upper jaw are built up, they become shifted nearer together and enclosed by a growing ridge of tissue, the prospective nose. At the close of the second month the nose is broad and flat, with the nostrils pointing forward rather than downward as they will later. The lower jaw is small and the chin is poorly developed. Seen in profile, the embryo looks almost chinless and revolt-

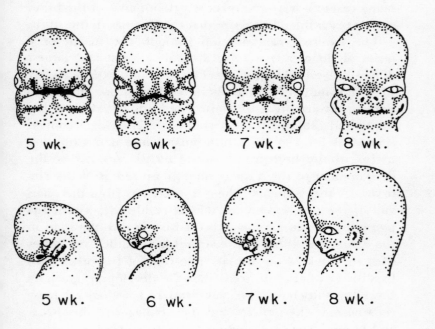

5 wk.   6 wk.   7 wk.   8 wk.

5 wk.   6 wk.   7 wk.   8 wk.

Fig. 11:

Development of the embryonic face during the second month of life. The drawings show front views (upper row) and side views (lower row) of embryonic heads in each successive week of the second month. (Based on Patten.)

ingly pug-nosed. The eyes are far apart and the prominent, bulging brain gives the embryo a very brainy
appearance. In fact it is interesting to note that the
embryo is truly 'brainy' in the sense that the brain forms
by far the largest part of the head. It will take the face
many years to overcome this early dominance of the brain
and to reach the relative size that the face has in the adult.

The external ears develop through the fusion of a
series of nodules that form around the first and largest
of the old gill-like grooves. The six nodules fuse slowly
to form a more or less recognizable human ear surrounding the groove that thus becomes converted into the
cavity and canal of the external ear. This frugal conversion of useless evolutionary remnants into new structures
useful to the human is a characteristic feature of the
development of the human embryo, as well as of the embryos of other animals. The outpocketings from the pharynx of the human embryo that resemble in position the
first gill slits of the fish are also reused, in this case to form
the Eustachian tubes that connect our middle ear cavities
with the back of the throat. The cells of the other "gill
bars" later migrate forward into the developing face and
form the muscles of the jaws and face; others of these
cells become the muscles and the cartilages of the throat
and larynx. Again as we saw in the development of three
successive forms of kidney, the human embryo retraces,
briefly and vaguely, part of the evolutionary history of
the human animal and then converts the nonhuman
structures to other distinctly human organs.

The limbs also pass through a surprising series of
changes during the second month. At the end of the
first month, the limb buds are small conical stubs project-
ing from the sides of the body (Fig. 8). During the second

month these limb buds elongate and differentiate into recognizable arms and legs (Fig. 10). Since the arm bud appears first and the leg bud later in the fourth week, the arm begins and completes each successive stage of differentiation slightly earlier than does the leg. Early in the fifth week the tip of each limb bud flattens to form a paddle-like ridge, the finger plate or toe plate (Fig. 12). Five parallel ridges, separated by shallow grooves, appear within each plate. The grooves gradually cut through between the ridges, marking off five stubby fingers or toes. The thumb and great toe early become widely separated from the other fingers and toes, sticking out from the side of the hand or foot in a way that suggests the grasping toes of tree-climbing animals. By the seventh week nail beds are forming near the ends of the fingers and toes, but true horny nails will not develop until the fifth month.

During the same period the elongating limbs become subdivided by constrictions that mark the level of elbow and knee, wrist and ankle. At first the elbow and knee both bend outwards, away from the sides of the body, and the palms and soles are turned inward facing the body. Not until the fourth month will the arms and legs be rotated into their final position so that the elbows bend backwards, the knees forward, and the soles face downward away from the body. Bones and muscles develop within the arms and legs during the last half of the second month, and near the end of the month it is probable that the arms and legs can be moved slightly. The arms are always farther along in development than the legs simply because they start their development sooner. Not until the third month do the legs become longer than the arms. From that time on, throughout the fetal period,

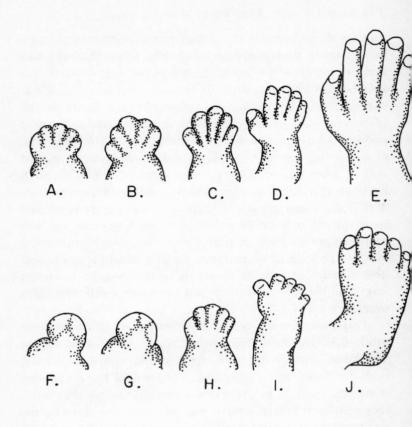

FIG. 12:

Development of the right hand (upper row) and right foot (lower row) of the human embryo during the second and third months. (Based on Patten.)

A and F. Fifth week.
B and G. Sixth week.
C and H. Seventh week.
D and I. Eighth week.
E and J. Third month.

childhood, and adolescence, the legs represent an increasingly greater proportion of the total length of the human body.

The smoothly rounded contours of the two-month-old embryo are but the outer evidence of the development of muscles beneath the skin. As the second month begins, the thin skin lies limp, molded into bulges and depressions by the underlying organs. By the end of the second month all of the large muscles typical of the human body have developed, forming a thick blanket of padding between the skin and the underlying organs. Some of the early muscle tissues invade the growing arms and legs and there differentiate into arm and leg muscles. The original blanket of muscles separates rapidly into many distinct muscles that become attached to the developing bones in such a way that the muscle fibers can move the bones when they contract. By the end of the second month the definitive pattern of muscles characteristic of the human body has been established and at least some of the muscles are capable of contracting. When two-month-old embryos are removed from the uterus, short, jerky movements of the arms and legs occur. Of course it is quite possible that the embryo would not have moved while it was living in the soothing warmth of the uterus, but the shock of being handled in removal from the uterus provokes unusual reactions in the delicate embryonic body. This observation is of interest since it shows that the embryonic muscles are capable of contracting. Perhaps those ancient philosophers who pondered on the time when human life begins would have called this first sign of the activity so typical of living man the beginning of life in the embryo.

Along with the muscles the bones develop, the skeleton to which the muscles are attached. Bone development in

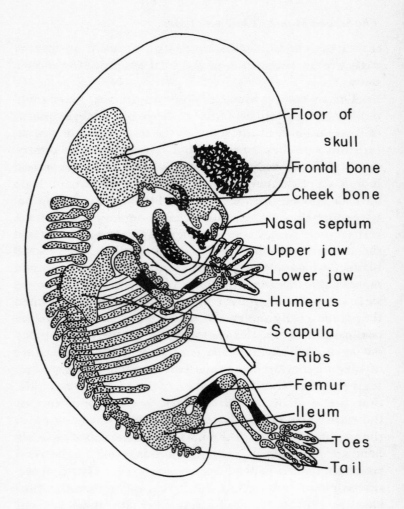

Floor of
skull
Frontal bone
Cheek bone
Nasal septum
Upper jaw
Lower jaw
Humerus
Scapula
Ribs
Femur
Ileum
Toes
Tail

FIG. 13:

Skeleton of a two-month-old human embryo. Cartilage parts are shown
in grey, bones in black. In the skull, face, and neck five membrane bones
have begun to develop (black and white). The bones of the arms and
legs are forming within and around the cartilage models of these bones.
This embryo was about one inch long in actual size.

56

the embryo is a peculiar process in which a pattern or model of the future bone is first formed in cartilage, a softer, more flexible material. After the model has been formed, rigid bony tissue is laid down around the cartilage model. As the sculptor first fashions his work in plastic clay and then, when he knows that his design is adequate, casts the statue in rigid bronze, so the developing embryo seems to plan out its skeleton in cartilage and then cast it in bone, removing the cartilage model as the bone is formed. However, such a model seems not to be essential for proper bone formation, since some parts of the human skeleton, such as many of the skull bones, are formed directly without the intervention of cartilage. Why some bones should first be formed in cartilage and others should not remains one of the mysteries of development, but the facts are that the bones of the trunk and limbs are pre-formed in cartilage while most of the flat bones of the skull and face are formed directly within membranes.

During the second month the cartilage models of all of the bones of the human skeleton develop (Fig. 13). Each cartilage model has the approximate shape and position that its descendant bone will have in the fully formed skeleton. Some of these cartilage models begin to be surrounded by rings of bone, while others are still completely cartilage. In addition, four membrane bones of the skull and face begin to form. But most of the skeleton of the two-month-old embryo consists of flexible cartilage, which offers some support for the soft body of the embryo but does not yet provide a rigid framework for muscle attachment.

Each cartilage model of a future bone is at first very small, since the entire embryo is small. As the embryo grows during the succeeding months of development, each

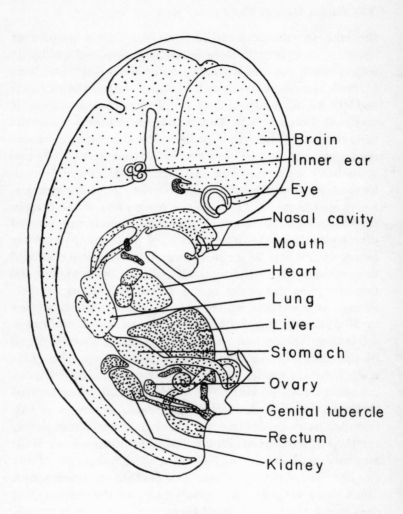

Brain
Inner ear
Eye
Nasal cavity
Mouth
Heart
Lung
Liver
Stomach
Ovary
Genital tubercle
Rectum
Kidney

Fig. 14:

Diagram of the major internal organs of a two-month-old female embryo. The head forms about half of the total length of the embryo. Note the protrusion of the intestine out into the base of the umbilical cord (normal umbilical hernia). This embryo was about one inch long in actual size.

cartilage also grows, retaining at all times the shape and position that its bone successor will have in the final human skeleton. Such growth of the cartilage elements of the skeleton continues after birth, throughout childhood and adolescence, until the individual attains his full size at maturity. Only then, to return to the analogy of the sculptor, is the skeleton fully cast in bone and the model discarded.

This "casting" process, or the replacement of the cartilage model with bone, also starts during the second month and continues until full growth is attained. A thin, narrow sheet of bone is laid down like a collar around the middle of each cartilage. Gradually this bony covering spreads farther and farther over the surface of the model, at the same time penetrating into the underlying cartilage. As this occurs, the cartilage degenerates and disappears, so that one may say that the model is not only surrounded by bone but displaced by bone. This displacement, a process called ossification, continues until each bone reaches its adult size. Then, the cartilage ceasing to grow, bone encroaches on the last bit of cartilage, the adult bone is completely formed, and no further growth occurs. The rate and sequence of ossification of the various bones of the skeleton varies with the sex of the individual, with ossification starting earlier and being completed sooner in girls than in boys.

The internal organs also undergo rapid growth and differentiation (Fig. 14). The brain forms one third of the body, by far the largest and most complex organ possessed by the two-month-old embryo. All of the nerves that join the brain and spinal cord with the muscles and sensory end organs of the skin have begun to form and some of them have begun to function. If the embryo is touched lightly on the face, the muscles of the body will contract and the embryo will move reflexively.

In the mouth all of the structures found in the adult have begun to form. The tongue is thrust up from the floor of the mouth as a wedge-shaped mass of skin and muscle that almost fills the mouth cavity. Taste buds, the sensory organs that enable us to sample flavors that enter the mouth, differentiate in the skin that covers the tongue and in the lining of the entire mouth cavity. The three pairs of salivary glands that will later begin to secrete saliva arise as downgrowths of the mouth lining into the underlying tissues. On the inner sides of the upper and lower jaws, circular grooves mark off the lips from the lining of the mouth, and just inside this lip groove the precursors of the teeth of the infant begin to form.

Within the embryonic throat two separate openings lead into the respiratory and digestive tracts. Immediately behind the tongue the glottis, a slitlike opening into the trachea, is guarded by a small flap of tissue, the epiglottis. From the back of the throat a wide round opening leads into the esophagus, the first part of the digestive tract. The esophagus, a narrow tube that leads to the stomach, is frequently plugged at this time as its lining cells grow faster than does the size of its cavity. But this temporary closure of the esophagus does no harm to the embryo, since it is not now attempting to swallow anything. Normally this closure of the esophagus is corrected by growth during the third month and the embryo is then able to swallow.

All of the organs concerned with digestion have developed. The expanded stomach lies behind the liver on the left side of the body. The long, coiled intestine is shoved out into the umbilical cord in a normal umbilical hernia. Within the intestine, the folded lining that will later serve to absorb food now fills the small cavity of the intestine so tightly that it too, like the esophagus, becomes plugged temporarily. It is indeed fortunate that the human embryo is not dependent on its own digestive tract for food at this time, since the plugged cavity would prevent proper passage of food along the length of the digestive tract.

The heart and lungs fill the chest cavity, which is separated from the abdominal cavity by a transverse muscular partition, the diaphragm. The heart, which was a simple bent tube in the first month of life, rapidly acquires its typical adult structure of four internal cavities, two atria and two ventricles, separated from each other by internal partitions or septa. The development of these internal septa within the heart during the second month of life makes this another critical stage in sensitivity to disturbance for the developing embryo. The heart septa develop in a complex manner during the sixth and seventh weeks of life (eighth and ninth weeks of pregnancy for the mother), and any serious disturbance of the environment of the embryo at this time is likely to affect the development of the heart. Normally the septum that divides the two ventricles from each other grows rapidly during these two weeks, gradually closing off the earlier opening between the two ventricles. If this closure is delayed or prevented from occurring, an opening may persist, permitting blood to leak through from the right ventricle to the left when the heart contracts. Such a ventricular hole is not serious for the embryo or fetus, who is being supplied with oxygen by the mother through the placenta. But it does become a serious handicap to the infant after birth, putting an extra burden on the heart and lungs when the infant has to get his own oxygen. The septum that divides the two atria from each other always has such a hole in the developing human embryo. This opening is normal and occurs in all human embryos, where it serves a useful function in allowing some of the blood being pumped from the heart to by-pass the useless lungs. This atrial opening normally closes soon after birth, but if it does not close properly it too, as is true of a ventricular hole, must be closed surgically.

All of the many other organs that will form a part of the mature human body have begun to develop by the end of the second month. The gonads, that will twenty years later give rise to the sex cells of this individual, start to differentiate and by the end of the second month of life it is possible for an embryologist to determine whether the immature embryo is potentially a male or female. But since the major events in the development of the sexual organs occurs during the third month, we shall reserve our description of sexual development for the next chapter of this biography. The various endocrine glands that will exercise so much control over the life of the developing individual both before his birth and during his entire life have begun to form but probably not to function. Above the kidney the large adrenal glands develop. Below the brain the master endocrine gland, the pituitary, lies attached to the floor of the brain. The thyroid gland forms a small mass of tissue lying in front of the trachea, and the thymus gland lies over the heart at the upper end of the chest cavity. Within the next two months of development each of these important endocrine glands will begin to secrete the hormones that control the growth and function of the other organs of the human body. But at this early stage of life, the human embryo is still dependent on its mother for such hormones as are needed for its development. It is not yet an independent human individual in any sense of the term, but a completely dependent parasite, controlled by the interaction of its own genes with the environment supplied as its first home by its mother.

So the second month of life closes with the stamp of human likeness clearly imprinted on the embryo. All of the organs that will serve him throughout his entire life have begun to form, and some have differentiated to the place where they are almost ready to begin functioning independently. So completely is the fundamental plan of the human body achieved by the two-month-old embryo that the biologist marks this as the end of the embryonic period of life. Within the normal span of human life each man is in turn an egg, embryo, fetus, infant, child, adolescent, and adult. At the end of the second month of life the first two stages have been completed. Henceforth the young human being is called a fetus.

CHAPTER 4

THE THIRD MONTH:

THE EMERGENCE OF SEX

Now THE HUMAN FETUS ENTERS a seven-month period of maturation, of the gradual development, practice, and perfection of its ability to live independently. In various mammals, the young are born at different stages in the process of their development. For example, the opposum gives birth to its offspring when they are barely as mature as the two-month human embryo; the newborn mouse and rat are blind, hairless, helpless creatures, little better prepared for independent life than the four-month-old human fetus. Man has extended the period of dependence of his young to nine months even though the human fetus is able to survive independently after about six months of development. But even after nine months of dependence on his mother for food and protection, the human infant is less well prepared to care for itself than are the young of many other mammals. So man extends the period of protection of his young even beyond the time of birth.

Now the new individual becomes marked with those distinguishing sexual traits that divide mankind into two classes, male and female. Although the sex of the individual was presumably determined at the moment of fertilization, when either an X-bearing or Y-bearing sperm

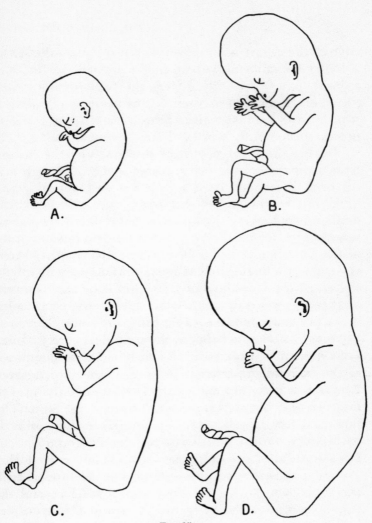

FIG. 15:

Development of the human fetus during the third month. Each fetus is
drawn at approximately its actual size. (Based on Patten.)
A. Nine weeks.
B. Ten weeks.
C. Eleven weeks.
D. Twelve weeks.

entered the egg, it is not possible to distinguish the sex of a living human embryo externally during the first two months of its life. Only during the third month, when the internal and external sex organs begin developing, is it possible to say that a given fetus has started on the long process of becoming a male or female human being.

During the third month of prenatal life, the human fetus grows from one inch to three inches in length and increases in weight from one gram to fourteen grams (Fig. 15). By the end of the month the fetus is slightly more human-looking than he was at the end of the second month, with his head now forming only about one third of the total length of his body, the trunk another third, and the legs a final third. As the trunk increases in length, the size of the abdominal cavity within it increases enough so that the protruding intestines are drawn back inside the fetal body and the disfiguring umbilical hernia is corrected. After this happens the umbilical cord becomes a slender, twisted rope of skin and blood vessels, attached to the body of the fetus at the site of the future navel. The skin is very thin and pliable, so the underlying ribs, muscles, and blood vessels shine through the skin. The arms and legs lengthen rapidly, and since there is little extra space within the uterus for them to occupy, they flex sharply at elbow and knee, wrist and ankle. So during the last six months of intra-uterine life the human fetus keeps his arms curled up close against his face and the legs bent against the belly in the typical fetal position.

The face continues remodeling the embryonic tissues around the mouth, eyes and nasal cavities and begins to overcome the early dominance of the brain part of the head. As the jaws and cheeks grow and the underlying bones give form and contours to the flat embryonic face,

66

the fetus begins to resemble a human infant. The eyes are gradually moved forward toward a position where binocular vision will become possible. The blind eyes are covered by the fused eyelids. The ears are slowly shifted higher on the head from their original position on either side of the lower jaw. The nose begins to build up as nasal cartilages form a bridge over the top of the nose and flaring alar wings at either side of the nostrils. The lips are marked off from the other skin of the face, and the groove in the center of the upper lip, the philtrum, is bounded by two ridges, the seams left from the fusion of the maxillary parts of the upper jaw with the median nasal process. Within the skin hair papillae start to form above the eyes and on the upper lip and chin, the first precursors of the facial hairs that will appear two months later.

Within the mouth the twenty baby teeth of the infant are marked out. From the dental plate that grew down into each jaw during the second month, twenty small inverted cups of specialized enamel-forming cells differentiate, each in the position where a tooth will form. Each enamel organ fits over the top of a small finger-like condensation of gum tissue, a dental papilla. During the next twelve months (six months of prenatal life and six months after birth) these twenty enamel organs and dental papillae will secrete enamel and dentine along the boundary between the two parts of each tooth bud, gradually building up the twenty baby teeth that will erupt through the infant's gums during the first three years of his life after birth. The future sockets for these teeth form as the developing jaw bones enclose the base of each dental papilla. The special minerals and vitamins needed for the synthesis of enamel and dentine must be supplied to the fetus through the placenta. The mother must therefore provide from her diet the extra minerals and vitamins that the fetus uses during the last seven months of development in the complex processes of forming, not only the enamel and dentine in the teeth, but also the chemically similar bones of the skeleton that are ossifying during this same period of growth.

Palate formation is another developmental process that may be influenced by the mother's diet and health during this time. Late in the second month two vertical curtains form from the inner sides of the upper jaws, hanging down from the roof of the mouth cavity on either side of the arched tongue. During the third month, as the lower jaw widens and the tongue is drawn down lower in the mouth cavity, these two palatine folds bend toward each other and grow together, forming a horizontal partition between the mouth cavity below and the nasal cavities above. When they fuse in the midline, in a seam whose scar remains in the roof of the mouth throughout life, a new roof of the mouth cavity has been formed. Bone develops in the front of this shelf, forming a bony palate behind the upper teeth, leaving the boneless soft palate to hang down toward the tongue as a curtain marking the back end of the mouth cavity. Sometimes this bending and fusion of the two halves of the palate fail to occur properly, and the resulting cleft palate incompletely separates nasal cavities from the mouth cavity. This defect, which may occur as a result of hereditary gene action or as a result of some unknown disturbance in the environment of the fetus during the third month, makes swallowing, breathing, and speech difficult for the affected infant. This defect is therefore usually corrected

68

by surgery to build up a complete partition between mouth and nasal cavities.

Although six months must pass before the first cry of the infant will be heard, the vocal cords whose vibrations produce such cries appear during the third month. At the upper end of the trachea three pairs of cartilages enclose the larynx, the voice box. Through the larynx must pass all of the air that enters or leaves the lungs. Partially spanning this narrow passageway are two transverse folds of tissue, the vocal cords. At first these cords are thick, soft, and lax, as ineffective as a broken string. At about the middle of pregnancy fine muscles and taut elastic tissue develop within the vocal cords, but even at birth the vocal cords are relatively thick and round-edged. Only during the first six months after birth do they take on the form of effective human vocal cords. It must be remembered that during the period of life lived within the uterus no air passes through the larynx to the lungs. The fetus lives in a watery world where breathing would flood the lungs with amniotic fluid. The first cry of the newborn child announces the initial passage of air through the larynx, to and from the lungs.

The digestive tract of the three-month fetus begins to show signs of activity, a practice period for the important role of digesting and absorbing food that will be its lifelong function. The salivary glands in the mouth start secreting saliva, and the gastric glands of the stomach start secreting mucus, the two slimy fluids that will act as lubricants for the passage of food down the digestive tract. By the end of the fourth month both of these sets of glands are also secreting the special enzymes, ptyalin in the saliva and pepsin in the gastric juice, that start the process of

69

digestion. The esophagus and intestine, whose small cavities are usually plugged during the second month, become open again, ready to serve as passageways for food. Muscles develop in the wall of the intestines and by the end of the third month peristalsis, the wavelike contraction that moves food through the intestine, has begun to occur.

The fetal liver begins to take over from the placenta a part of the job of synthesizing the special chemicals that this fetus needs for its individual growth. It also assumes one of its major functions, the storage of the excess nutritive chemicals that are taken into the body intermittently at meal times, and must be saved and parcelled out continuously to the tissues of the body between meals. The liver now starts one of its important but temporary functions, the formation of new blood cells to replace the blood cells that die and are destroyed. Human blood cells are highly specialized, short-lived cells that perform their complex tasks as conveyors, protectors, and scavengers of the body for only a few weeks, and they must be replaced constantly in the fetus, child, or the adult. The first human blood cells were formed during the third and fourth weeks of life in the vestigial, temporary yolk sac. During the second month blood cells are formed in numerous scattered blood islands throughout the embryonic tissues, but by the third month the liver becomes the dominant site of blood cell formation. Within the next month the liver blood islands begin to regress and the spleen takes over the major part of blood cell formation. Before birth and throughout independent life, most blood cells are formed in the marrow tissue of the bones, but the liver and spleen remain capable of resuming their fetal roles of blood cell formation if the need arises.

70

The kidneys also start functioning during the third month, secreting a dilute urine that trickles down the ducts connecting the kidneys with the bladder. Eventually this urine seeps out of the outlet of the bladder into the amniotic fluid that surrounds the fetus. The first two attempts at kidney formation have by now failed completely, and the pronephros and mesonephros have degenerated. The final true kidney, the metanephros, has begun to develop the special secretory tubules whose function it is to remove unwanted waste products from the fetal blood as it flows through the kidney, and to concentrate these waste products into urine. Although the human kidney begins to function during the third month of life, it is by no means a fully developed organ. New excretory tubules continue to be formed within the growing kidney not only during the remaining six months before birth but also during the first month after birth. It must be remembered that most of the waste products of the fetal body are passed out through the placenta into the mother's blood, to be excreted as a part of the mother's urine. Perhaps this early unnecessary excretion of urine through the poorly developed fetal kidney might be viewed as an apprenticeship, a safety period during which the still incomplete kidney can gradually acquire and perfect its important function of waste elimination before complete independence is forced on the new human being.

But overshadowing the slow development of the kidney during this third month are the kaleidoscopic changes that occur in the sexual organs of the fetus. During the first month of life all human embryos appear to be alike in structure and development, regardless of whether they are genetically male or female in sex. Even in the second month of life there is at first no way of telling the sex of

71

the individual except by the difficult method of counting the chromosomes. But by the beginning of the third month, the developing gonads can be identified in microscopic study as being either potentially testis or ovary, and by the end of the third month the rapidly developing male penis clearly distinguishes the male fetus from the more slowly developing female. Perhaps the most interesting aspect of sexual development is the fact that the first steps in the process are always nonsexual in nature, that is to say the first formed organs are identical in the two sexes. Nature seems to lay down in each individual all of the sexual organs of the race, and then by emphasizing certain of these organs and allowing the others to degenerate, transforms the sexually neuter embryo into a typical male or female individual.

Sexual development begins in the sixth week of life when the indifferent gonads form as thickened masses of tissue lying along the surface of the mesonephros. The tissues within this primitive gonad are at first identical in appearance in all embryos, regardless of their potential sex. The cells covering the surface of the gonad proliferate, giving rise to cords of primary sexual cells that wind through the underlying connective tissues. By the end of the second month, these first genital cords become quite distinct and sharply cut off from the surface if the embryo is a male, and the gonad can then be identified as a developing testis. However if these earliest cords do not become distinct at this time, the embryo is either a slow male or a female. During the third month, in a prospective female fetus, these first male-like sex cords are abandoned in the center of the gonad and the surface covering starts afresh on a new proliferation of sexual cells. The descendants of this second attempt will eventually become the sex cells of the fetal ovary. Thus we might say that at the heart of every fetal ovary there lies an undeveloped testis, and the female gonads represent the proverbial last word, if not an improvement over the male, at least the result of a second trial.

Related to this bisexual development of the gonads is a similar bisexual development of the genital ducts (Fig. 16). In the two-month-old embryo of either sex, two sets of possible sexual ducts develop: the Wolffian ducts that drain the mesonephros during the short time when it functions; and a second pair of ducts, the Mullerian ducts, that form near the gonads and run parallel with the Wolffian ducts, fusing in the pelvic region to form a single duct. Embryos of both sexes develop both sets of ducts during the neuter stage of their sexual development, even though the Wolffian ducts will become only the sperm ducts of the male and the Mullerian ducts will be useful only to the female fetus. When the indifferent gonad becomes a definitive testis in the third month, the Mullerian ducts begin to degenerate in the male, leaving only fragments of their upper and lower ends to form vestigial tags attached to the testes, and a small, useless vagina masculinis embedded in the wall of the male urethra. In the female fetus when the gonad becomes an ovary during the third month, the Wolffian ducts degenerate, again leaving only remnants as reminders of the earlier bisexual condition. The Mullerian ducts, on the other hand, continue to develop and become the Fallopian tubes, uterus and vagina, the reproductive tract of the female.

Thus in each human embryo, regardless of its sex, two pairs of possible sex ducts are developed. As the gonads develop the specific characteristics of one sex, the ducts of that sex continue to grow and differentiate, while the ducts

73

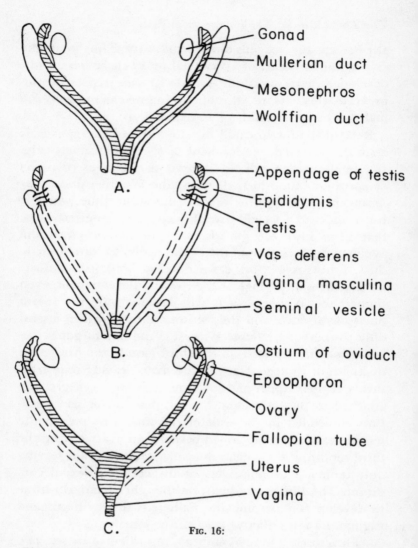

Gonad
Mullerian duct
Mesonephros
Wolffian duct

A.

Appendage of testis
Epididymis
Testis
Vas deferens
Vagina masculina
Seminal vesicle

B.

Ostium of oviduct
Epoophoron
Ovary
Fallopian tube
Uterus
Vagina

C.   FIG. 16:

Diagrams showing the transformation of the double sets of sex ducts of the indifferent period (A) into the typical sex ducts of the male fetus (B) and the female fetus (C). The Mullerian ducts and their derivatives are cross-hatched. Degenerating structures are shown in broken lines.

74

of the opposite sex degenerate. The cause of these reactions of the sex ducts is not definitely known, but it is
believed that the fetal testis secretes some kind of male
sex hormone that promotes the development of the male
ducts and suppresses the development of the Mullerian
ducts. In the female fetus there is no clear evidence that
the fetal ovary secretes female sex hormones at this early
time, and it is postulated that the mere absence of the
male sex hormones prevents the Wolffian ducts from per-
sisting when the mesonephros degenerates, while the Mullerian ducts possess an inherent ability to develop unless
they are inhibited by the presence of male sex hormones.

The external sex organs, the genitalia, undergo a
similar and parallel bisexual history (Fig. 17). During
the second month all embryos possess a conical tubercle
of skin and underlying tissues, forming on the belly wall
between the umbilical cord and the legs. On the under
side of this genital tubercle lies the common outlet of the
duct from the bladder (Fig. 14). This opening is given
the double name of urogenital sinus because the ureters,
carrying urine from the kidneys, and the Wolffian and
Mullerian ducts, all open into a common outlet at this
stage. When the testis develops in the male fetus and
begins secreting male sex hormones, the genital tubercle
starts enlarging and its tip begins to swell into a round,
terminal knob (Fig. 17b). The tissues on either side of
the urogenital sinus rise up in two parallel urogenital folds
enclosing the urogenital sinus. These two folds then fuse,
enclosing the urogenital sinus as a tube, the male urethra,
which opens to the outside just below the glans on the
end of the penis. The seam of fusion of the urogenital folds
forms a visible scar on the under side of the male penis.
The genital swellings continue to expand, forming two

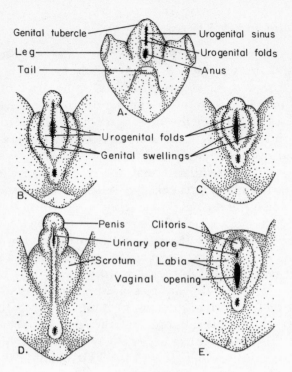

Genital tubercle — — Urogenital sinus
Leg — — Urogenital folds
Tail — — Anus

A.

— Urogenital folds
— Genital swellings

B.   C.

— Penis   Clitoris —
— Urinary pore —
— Scrotum   Labia —
— Vaginal opening —

D.   E.

FIG. 17:

Development of the external sex organs of the human embryo during
the second and third months. In each diagram only the genital and anal
regions of the body are shown, viewed from below. (Based on Patten.)
A. Seven weeks. Male and female embryos have identical external sex
organs.
B. Male fetus at ten weeks. The genital tubercle is becoming an elongate
penis; the urogenital folds are fusing to enclose the urethra of the penis.
Two genital swellings form on either side of the penis.
C. Female fetus at ten weeks. The genital tubercle remains small; the
urogenital folds do not fuse; the genital swellings are small.
D. Male fetus at twelve weeks. The penis is longer and the urethral seam
is closed almost to the level of the glans penis. The genital swellings have
enlarged to form the scrotum.
E. Female fetus at twelve weeks. The genital tubercle becomes the small
clitoris. The urogenital folds and the genital swellings form two sets of
lips, the labia, surrounding the separate openings of the urethra and
vagina.

76

sacs of body wall on either side of the penis. These empty sacs also fuse with each other along a median seam, forming the prospective scrotum. Near the end of prenatal life the testes, which originally lie up in the abdominal cavity, descend internally through the pelvis and move out into these two scrotal sacs along a narrow canal that becomes the inguinal canal of the mature male.

The female embryo begins its external organs with the same precursors as does the male. But in the female, where no male sex hormones are formed, the genital tubercle does not enlarge significantly, but remains small to form the clitoris, the diminutive female homologue of the penis. The urogenital folds form as they do in the male fetus, but they do not fold over and fuse to enclose the urogenital sinus. Instead they remain as open folds or lips enclosing the open urogenital sinus. Internally in the female the urethra from the bladder and the fused lower end of the Mullerian duct, the vagina, become separated from each other so that they now open separately into the old urogenital sinus, which in the mature female is called the vestibule. The genital swellings which in the male enlarge to form the scrotum do not enlarge in the female but persist as low swellings on either side of the vestibule. These genital swellings then become a second pair of lips, the labia majora, which lie outside of the inner lips formed from the old urogenital folds. The female fetus thus resembles an undeveloped male, since the various precursors from which the male genitalia are fashioned retain their early embryonic condition in the female. By the end of the third month a properly developing male fetus is thus clearly identifiable by his enlarging penis, closed urethral folds, and swollen scrotal sacs. Those fetuses that do not show these masculine traits are probably females, although sometimes it is difficult to be sure that the fetus is not simply a delayed, slowly developing male.

Thus during the second and third months of life each human being passes through a series of complex developmental processes that change him from a sexually neuter embryo, possessing all of the basic structures necessary for the development of both the male and female sexual organs, into an irrevocably marked male or female possessing only those organs that will become functional parts of the mature reproductive system. This dual potentiality of sexual development raises several intriguing questions concerning the nature and development of sex. Is each person fundamentally bisexual, with the organs and functions of the apparent sex holding in abeyance the undeveloped characters of the opposite sex? Are maleness and femaleness completely distinct patterns of structure, irrevocably imprinted on the indifferent embryo in the second month of life, or do the typical male and female represent opposite extremes in the development of a single but complex system of sexual characters?

Studies of sexual development in man and animals have disclosed scattered facts bearing on these problems. Sometimes in cattle twin calves that are genetically male and female develop in such close proximity within the uterus that their two placentae become joined. The blood of one fetus is thus able to circulate through the body of its twin. When this happens, the supposedly female calf develops as an intersex called a freemartin. It is believed that in such cases the male calf, developing its testes earlier than the female develops her ovaries, secretes male sex hormones that pass into the female where they suppress the development of female sexual structure and encourage

78

the development of some male structures. There is no known evidence that a similar sex reversal can occur in human development, but it is known that in some human beings certain characteristics of the opposite sex can develop simultaneously with the genetically determined sexual structures. Such cases indicate that there are various degrees of sexual development even in man. All of these facts do not vitiate the well-established theory that the sex of the individual is determined by the chromosomes present in the sperm at the time of fertilization. Under normal circumstances such is clearly the case. But the process through which the specific sexual organs are formed is clearly a complex one that begins with a bisexual stage, progresses along diverging paths in which the organs of one sex or the other become dominant. Variations in the degree, the direction, and the speed of sexual development are embryologically quite possible. Masculinity and feminity are both a result of our developmental biography.

Now the human fetus begins to move spontaneously, provoked to activity by some unknown inner tensions. These first movements are rarely perceived by the mother since the small fetus is insulated from her body by the water-jacket of amniotic fluid. But it is known that the three-month-old fetus does move, and if it is removed from the uterus and tested for response to touch, it will curl its fingers into a tiny fist when the palm is tickled, or curl its toes downward in the Babinski reflex that marks the immature infant. The fetal heart beat becomes strong enough to be heard through the walls of the mother's uterus and abdomen, giving the doctor unmistakable evidence that a living fetus is developing within the pregnant uterus.

CHAPTER 5

THE FOURTH MONTH:
THE QUICKENING

DEATH THROWS ITS SHADOW over man before he is born, for the stream of life flows most swiftly through the embryo and young fetus and then inexorably slows down, even before birth. If time is measured for living creatures by internal events and changes, then half a lifetime is lived during our first two months of life. We experience far greater and more rapid changes during those first two months than will ever again occur throughout our entire life, and each event molds us irrevocably into the kind of human being we can or cannot become.

The rate of growth and change begins to slow down during the remaining seven months of intra-uterine life (Fig. 18). The human fetus triples its size in the third month, and doubles it during the fourth month, when it grows from three to six inches in length. By the end of the fifth month the fetus is about ten inches long, half the average length of the newborn infant. During the remaining four months of prenatal life, we grow almost an inch in height every ten days. If we continued to grow at this rate after birth, a ten-year-old child would be twenty feet tall. Our weight increases rapidly from about one half a pound at five months to six pounds at birth. It has been estimated that if we continued to gain weight

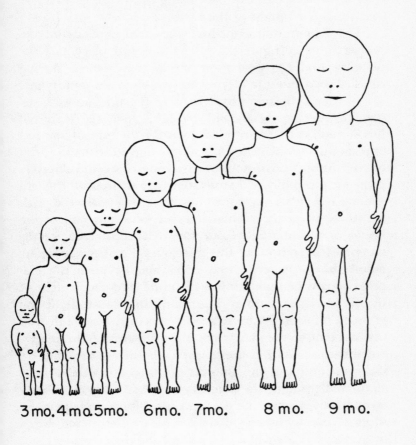

3 mo. 4 mo. 5 mo.   6 mo.   7 mo.   8 mo.   9 mo.

Fig. 18:

Fetuses of the third through ninth months of development, all drawn
to one-fifth natural height, to show the growth and changing proportions
of the body. (Based on Scammon and Calkins.)

at this rate, one adult human being would weigh two million times the weight of the earth.

This astounding growth of the fetus depends on the proper functioning of the fully developed placenta. The placenta undergoes its most rapid development during the first two months of pregnancy, when the embryonic trophoblast cells aggressively invade the uterine wall, destroying uterine tissues and breaking open the maternal blood vessels in the invaded area. By the end of the second month the placenta fills about one third of the wall of the uterus and the maternal tissues have developed a protective capsule of connective tissues around this invader. The placenta continues to grow until the fifth month of pregnancy, when it involves almost half of the lining of the uterus. At one month the placenta weighs six times as much as the developing embryo; at four months they are equal in weight; and by birth the placenta weighs one pound, less than one sixth the weight of the infant it is feeding. The mounting demands of the growing fetus on the more slowly growing placenta during the last half of pregnancy poses a problem for the maternal organism. As the uterus grows in size to accomodate the growing fetus, the amount of maternal blood that is circulated through the placenta increases. But eventually a time arrives when the placenta is no longer adequate to support the increasing demands of the fetus and birth must occur.

The human fetus is not simply a miniature man, needing only steady growth to become a normal human being, but a gnome-like creature whose head is too large, trunk too broad, and legs too short. This disproportion becomes evident if the embryo, fetus, infant, child, adolescent and adult, each in his own proper internal proportions, are drawn to the same height (Fig. 19). At two months the head forms almost one half of the entire body; from the third to fifth months it is one third; at birth one fourth; and in the adult about one tenth of the total body height. This does not mean, of course, that the head is not continually growing but merely that it had a 'head start' over the remainder of the body. The legs, on the other hand, form less than one fourth of the height at two months, one third at five months, two fifths at birth, and more than one half of the total height of an adult man. Both the trunk and arms reach their proper proportions fairly early in life, but both become progressively more slender and shapely.

By the fourth month of development, the growing fetus, its placenta, and the fluid-filled amniotic sac surrounding the fetus, together begin to stretch the mother's uterus markedly. The pregnant uterus begins to project up out of the pelvic cavity, where the uterus normally lies, and invades the mother's abdominal cavity. As the abdominal organs are crowded by the growing uterus, the abdominal wall begins to stretch and protrude, giving external evidence of the fetus growing within the uterus. The uterus itself grows in size, weight, and the thickness of its muscular wall during the last half of pregnancy. By the sixth month the apex of the expanding uterus reaches to the level of the mother's navel, and by the ninth month it is almost against the ribs and diaphragm. This growth of the uterus, along with the growth of the fetus, the placenta, and the increasing amount of amniotic fluid, all add together to produce an increase in the mother's apparent weight during the last half of pregnancy.

The four-month human fetus begins to practice some of the activities that will be required of him in indepen-

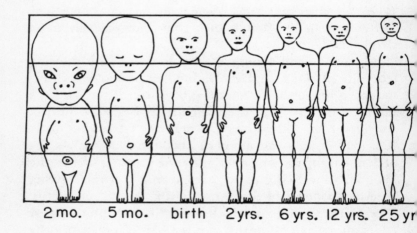

2 mo.   5 mo.   birth   2 yrs.   6 yrs.   12 yrs.   25 yr

FIG. 19:

A composite diagram to show the changing proportions of the human body during its entire development. Embryo, fetus, infant, child, adolescent, and adult, each in its proper internal proportions, have all been drawn to the same height. (Based on Scammon and Stratz.)

84

dent life. Most of the muscles of both the outer body wall and the wall of the digestive tract have developed to the point where they now become functional, able to contract in coordinated patterns to produce useful movements. The fetus begins to suck and swallow intermittently, the beginning of the feeding reflexes that the infant must use to obtain food. Since the fetus is living in a watery bath of amniotic fluid, whenever he opens his mouth he swallows some amniotic fluid. This fluid is then moved along the esophagus to the stomach, where marked muscular contractions, similar to the hunger contractions of the newborn infant, occur. In the stomach and intestine the water and some of the other chemicals present in the amniotic fluid are absorbed through the wall of the digestive tract into the fetal blood stream, where they are circulated through the growing fetal body and used as an auxiliary source of food. Some of this swallowed amniotic fluid may then be excreted through the fetal kidneys, passed through the fetal bladder, and leak out into the amniotic sac again as part of the fetal urine. Thus a circular movement of water occurs through the fetus, from the amniotic fluid into the fetus and then back into the amniotic fluid. The original source of this water is of course the mother's intake of water, its transmission through the placenta to the fetal blood stream, and its diffusion through the fetal body and out into the amniotic sac. Studies with tracer chemicals that can be identified have shown that the amniotic fluid is being constantly changed, continually added to and removed. In some cases the amount of amniotic fluid becomes so great that the mother's abdomen is uncomfortably stretched. If this becomes serious, a sweet sugar solution can be injected into the amniotic fluid through the abdominal and uterine walls. The fetus then begins to swallow the amniotic fluid faster, reducing its amount. This intriguing experiment suggests that the fetus can distinguish sweet from bitter, and comes to prefer the sweet even before birth.

While the fetus is living in its watery world, it has no need to breathe, and if it did the amniotic fluid would simply flood the lungs with water. The lungs are poorly developed at this time, but the muscles of the rib cage and diaphragm have developed to the point where they can contract and produce breathing movements of the chest. If a four-month fetus is removed from the uterus surgically, it may gasp a few times and show slight breathing movements of the chest wall. But true breathing cannot be initiated or maintained at this early stage of development, and the fetus cannot survive outside of the uterus or cut off from the placenta.

Now the still, silent march of the fetus along the road from conception to birth becomes enlivened and quickened. Between quiet, motionless periods of sleep, the fetus wakes and begins to move spontaneously. He stirs, stretches, and vigorously thrusts out his arms and legs. The first movements perceived by the mother may seem to her like a faint fluttering of wings, but before long his blows against the walls of the uterus inform her in unmistakable terms that life is beating at the door of the womb. For this is the time of the "quickening in the womb" of folklore.

CHAPTER 6

THE FIFTH MONTH:
INDIVIDUALITY

MAN IS AN ENIGMA; he is both one and many, individual yet complex. He is composed of billions of cells that are constantly dying and being replaced, yet he maintains a mysterious unity that we call individuality. A continuous stream of inanimate material flows through the enclosed space that he calls his body, becoming momentarily alive and then passing back into the external world, yet the continuity that he calls his life persists unbroken from conception to death.

What is this individuality that marks each man as being unique? What features of human life before birth make even the five-month-old fetus visibly individual and different from every other human fetus, even a twin brother or sister living in the same uterus at the same time? What mysterious force counteracts the separateness of the differentiating cells, tissues and organs of the developing fetus, and unifies their activities into one integrated pattern of growth and development, one unique human life? These questions confront the embryologist studying the development of man before birth as seriously as they plague the philosopher studying the nature of human life after birth.

The individuality of each human being is determined

during his prenatal life just as clearly as his body is formed through the processes of development. The genes that are present in the fertilized egg determine what future activities are possible for that egg, and the genes that are absent set the limits of what is impossible for each individual. Scientists do not yet know exactly how the genes influence the sequence of changes in form, position, and structure that occur within the cells of the developing embryo. But they do know that these changes depend on the continuous interaction of the living cell with its immediate environment within the embryo, with the total environment provided by the mother's uterus, and with the control processes that operate within the living embryo to integrate all of its activities in a way that will benefit the whole embryo. Each developing cell absorbs nonliving food materials from its environment, synthesizes these chemicals into specific components of its own living substances under the control of its own genes, and gives off by-products that then become part of the environment of adjacent cells. Each event that occurs to a given cell changes that cell from what it was before that event, and the next event that occurs is determined by the preceding history of that cell. Because the environment and the eventful history of each living cell is different, the cells change in a gradual process of differentiation and each change then becomes the cause for further changes.

The development of the human embryo is therefore a dynamic historical process in which each action, change, or event determines the future nature of the embryo. Living organisms might be called time-binding machines, in which past events determine the present and the future, and the nature of the individual at any given moment in his life is dependent on all of his previous history. Individuality is at least in part the sum of the past events in the life of each living organism, whether it be embryo, fetus, infant, child or adult. By the fifth month of life the individual history of the human fetus has led to the development of distinctive features of form, proportion, structure, and function that make the fetus individually recognizable. Even identical twins, who start life with identical sets of genes, still experience enough environmental and historical differences during the first five months of their lives within the same uterus to become individually different.

The unity of the developing organism is more than simply the unity of time and space. The many cells that make up the human body are all descendants by mitosis of the same fertilized egg, and are therefore all of about the same age. They lie adjacent to each other, forming the single mass of the developing human body. As development progresses, the individual cells become increasingly different from each other in structure and function, yet all of them seem to be controlled at all times by some unknown unifying force, so that the development and function of each part of the embryo contributes to the welfare of the entire embryo. If this unifying principle fails to operate properly, then the growth or development of one part may forge ahead or lag behind the development of other parts, and the whole fetus will become abnormal and usually die. The nature of this unifying force in the very young embryo remains unknown. When the heart, blood, and circulatory system develop, these serve to provide a relatively uniform environment for all of the cells of the body, thus helping to maintain unanimity. The nervous system—the brain, spinal cord, and the nerves that grow out to all of the organs and parts of the body—later helps to provide a common background of stimulus or inhibition for the various organs of the body. Still later in development, the endocrine glands of the fetus begin secreting the chemical hormones that are carried throughout the growing body, where they control the growth and functions of many of the fetal organs. All of these control mechanisms act together to maintain a steady state of balance within the complex body of the fetus during the last five months of prenatal life and during all of life after birth.

The human body may be compared to a cooperative society whose members band together for mutual support and protection, presenting a common front to the external world, and sharing equally in the privileges and responsibilities of their internal world. Division of labor, specialization, and the exchange of produce are just as important in the society of cells and organs as in the society of men. Certain organs specialize in converting the materials taken in as food into usable components of living cells; these are the digestive organs. The circulating fluids of the body form an extensive transportation system. Nerves are the cables of the communication system, while the brain acts as the central exchange through which activities in widely separated regions are correlated and controlled. The potent endocrine glands might be called the supervisors of the body since their secretions determine the speed and constancy of many activities. Overlying all of these specialized systems is the skin—the protector, conservator, and reporter of the society of organs.

The skin of the young embryo is a thin, soft, fragile layer of cells that does little more than cover the internal organs. By the fifth month of life the skin begins to thicken to form a dense, layered covering that effectively protects the internal organs. Its outermost layers begin to change into flattened dead cornified cells that after birth will form an impervious protective layer over the entire surface of the body. These dead surface cells are continuously sloughed off the surface of the fetal skin into the amniotic fluid that surrounds the fetus, where they gradually accumulate to form a cheesy coating of dead cells and oil from the skin glands that is called the vernix caseosa. The thickness of the surface layer of cornified cells varies in different parts of the human skin, being thickest on the palms of the hands and the soles of the feet. One might think that these semi-calloused surfaces become thickened as a result of pressure or abrasion, but in fact the palms and soles begin to be greatly thickened even in the five-month-old fetus, who is certainly not subjected to any special pressures on his hands or feet while he floats in the cushioning amniotic fluid. So it must be our human genes, inherited from ancestors who needed thickened pads on their hands and feet for protection, that produce this cornification of the palms and soles even in the quiet fetus long before such protection is needed.

The skin of the fetus is thrown into minute folds that project down into the underlying connective tissues, and into ridges that form complex whorls and lines on the surface of the fingers and toes, palms and soles. The pattern of these skin ridges is individual and characteristic even in the five-month fetus, so that fingerprints and footprints serve to identify each individual human being even before birth.

Other downgrowths from the inner surface of the skin develop into oil glands, sweat glands, and hair follicles. The oil glands begin secreting a fatty waste product that accumulates over the surface of the fetal skin to form the cheesy vernix caseosa. Sweat glands begin slowly to secrete sweat, a dilute form of urine. After birth the evaporation of the watery part of the sweat from the surface of the skin serves to cool the body and to help maintain the constant body temperature characteristic of all warm-blooded animals. In the fetus the sweat glands are only poorly developed, and the complex nervous reflexes that increase or inhibit sweat formation, depending on the temperature of the body and the air that surrounds it, are poorly developed. The human fetus, if born prematurely, has poor control of its internal temperature because its sweating reflexes are not yet well developed.

Hair is a characteristic skin structure of all mammals, including man, forming a more or less complete insulating hair coat over most of the body. Hair follicles begin to develop in the three-month fetus as tubular downgrowths of the skin. The first hair follicles form above the eyes in the future eyebrow region, on the upper lip and chin, and later over the scalp. During the fourth month hair follicles form over the entire body, and within each follicle a fine, slender shaft of hair begins to grow. By the end of the fifth month a blanket of soft fetal hair, called lanugo, erupts over the back, arms and legs of the fetus. Gradually hairs appear more sparsely over the entire body. The scalp hairs and eyebrows are heavier than the fine lanugo and soon form distinctive head hair and eyebrows. The lanugo hair forms a thick, downy covering over the fetal skin during the last three months of prenatal life, when it is constantly being formed, sloughed off into the vernix caseosa, and replaced by new hairs. The lanugo coat is largely lost before birth, to be replaced gradually by the heavier but sparser body hairs of the infant. The first hairs have little pigment in them, but as new generations of hair develop, pigment increases progressively and the hair becomes darker in color unless the individual does not have the proper genes for pigmentation. The skin in general, as well as the hair, has little pigmentation in the fetus, so that even infants of dark-skinned ancestry are light-skinned at birth. Pigmentation increases rapidly after birth, and both the skin and the hair darken progressively.

Horny nails on the tips of fingers and toes are another characteristic of mammals. Nails consist of a thickened sheet of dead horny cells that is formed continuously from a deep fold of skin, the nail fold. The nail grows outward along a specialized nail bed, and projects free beyond the tip of the finger or toe. Nail folds start to form soon after the fingers and toes are carved out of the hand and foot plates (Fig. 12). By five months the surface of the nail bed begins to keratinize, forming a false nail. Not until the sixth month of development do true nails begin to grow out over the surface of the fingers and toes. These fetal nails grow rather slowly, reaching the ends of the fingers and toes only in the nine-month fetus. At first the nail is covered by a thin, tough layer of cells similar to the cuticle of the mature nail. This covering is usually sloughed off before birth, although at times remnants of it are seen in the newborn infant. The fetal and infant nails are thin and relatively soft compared to the hard, firm, thick nails of the adult. By birth the nails sometimes project beyond the tips of the fingers and toes and need to be trimmed at once.

The internal organs show marked changes in relative position and size during the course of fetal development. Such changes are best illustrated by a series of diagrams of embryos and fetuses all brought to the same height (Fig. 20). The most striking feature of such a series is the

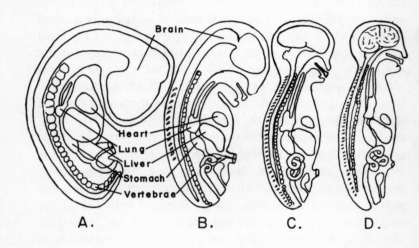

Brain

Heart
Lung
Liver
Stomach
Vertebrae

A.   B.   C.   D.

FIG. 20:

Diagrams of fetuses of two months (A), three months (B), five months
(C), and nine months (D), all brought to the same height. The major
internal organs are shown in their proper relative size and position.
(Adapted from Arey.)

straightening of the body axis. Early in the second month the embryo forms almost a closed circle, with his tail not far from his head. At three months the head has been raised considerably and the back forms a shallow curve. At five months the head is erectly balanced on the newly formed neck and the back is still less curved. At birth the head is perfectly erect and the back is almost unbelievably straight. In fact it is more nearly straight than it will ever again be, for as soon as the child learns to sit and walk, secondary curvatures appear in the spinal column as aids to balance.

Thoughtful examination of this series of diagrams will show that the reason the two-month-old embryo curves is that it consists of almost all back and very little front. In fact from the crown of the head to the tip of the tail the embryo measures twice as much along the back as along the front. On the front the face, neck, abdomen, and pelvis are poorly developed, while on the back all of the thirty-three or more segments that will form the vertebrae and back muscles have developed. When in the third month the face and chest wall, and in the fifth month the neck, abdomen and pelvic walls are built up, the fetus straightens out.

A second striking feature shown in these diagrams is the decreasing prominence of the head, particularly of the brain. At two months the brain occupies almost half of the total length of the embryo. At three months it forms less than one third, and at birth one fourth of the total height. Although the brain increases in complexity of form and internal structure, and of course actually grows in size, it forms a steadily less prominent part of the human body. Accompanying this relative decrease in the size of the brain goes a less marked decrease in prominence of the entire head. Within the head there is a continual emergence of the face, especially of the jaws, as compared with the cranial part of the head.

In the trunk a curious phenomenon results from the early disproportion of back and belly sides. The internal organs, developing at a time when there is little space within the still undeveloped belly, occupy their proper positions relative to each other, but relative to the back they lie far from their ultimate location. The heart and lungs develop in the region of the future neck; the liver and stomach in the future chest region; and the unbilical cord lies at the level of the future diaphragm. The abdomen and pelvis are so small as to be practically non-existent.

Then as the belly wall is built up, the internal organs come to lie at lower and lower levels relative to the backbone. At three months the heart lies in the upper chest region; at birth it lies at the bottom of the chest. The liver and stomach move down out of the chest into the enlarging abdomen. This gradual shift downward in the position of the internal organs, called the descent of the viscera, is not completed until after birth. For example, the bladder and uterus do not descend from the abdomen into the pelvis until after birth.

This descent of the viscera during development leads to one of the curious features of human anatomy. The nerves to all the major internal organs grow from the spinal cord to the major organs early in the second month, when the various organs lie high up in the fetal body. As the organs descend gradually into the newly formed thoracic, abdominal and pelvic cavities, their nerves are dragged along after them. The result is that in the adult human the nerves to the heart and diaphragm, for ex-

96

ample, arise from the spinal cord in the neck region, wind their way down through all the organs of the chest until they finally reach the heart and diaphragm at the bottom of the chest. All of the nerves to the internal visceral organs are similarly long and wandering, arising from the spinal cord far above the level of the organ that they innervate. The spinal cord itself reaches its full growth in length quite early in development, and then becomes relatively shorter and shorter, with the result that by birth the end of the spinal cord lies up in the lumbar region of the vertebral column, and the nerves to the legs arise above the top of the pelvic bones.

The five-month fetus moves actively and frequently in short periods of wakefulness between longer periods of sleep. He swallows the amniotic fluid, along with the sloughed-off skin cells, lanugo hairs and fatty vernix caseosa that float in it. Within the stomach and intestines this material is churned about by peristalsis, the water and some of the chemicals are digested and absorbed into the fetal blood stream, and the undigestible remains begin to accumulate in the fetal large intestine as a viscous, odorless fetal feces, called meconium. The liver begins to secrete bile into the small intestine, and the accumulating bile pigments color the meconium a dark green color. Usually this meconium is retained in the intestines until after birth, but occasionally it may be defecated out through the anus into the amniotic sac.

Most of the fetal organs have begun to practice their typical functions by the fifth month, but the fetus is not yet mature enough to live independently. If born, or strictly speaking aborted, it may live for a few minutes, take a few breaths, and perhaps cry. But it soon gives up the struggle and dies. Although the five-month human fetus is able to move actively, it is unable to maintain the complex reflex movements necessary for sustained breathing. Some vital functions, perhaps of the brain, of the nervous reflexes, or even of the lung itself, are still too poorly developed to carry their share of the burden of independent life.

CHAPTER 7

THE SIXTH MONTH:

THE SENSES

BY THE END of the sixth calendar month of human pregnancy the fetus is about twenty-five weeks old and has completed two thirds of its normal prenatal life. During the sixth month it grows about three inches to be about thirteen inches long, and gains about one pound to weigh approximately two pounds by the end of the month. During this month the fetus is "previable" in the sense that it is not yet able to live independently, but soon after the end of this month the human infant can survive if born prematurely. The six-month-old fetus bears a reasonable resemblance to a normal human infant in spite of its small size (Fig. 21). Its body has now straightened out from the embryonic curl of its earlier life, and its head, now covered with hair, is held erect on a slender neck. Eyebrows and eyelashes frame the eyes, and by the end of this month the eyelids, which were fused shut during the preceding three months, become free to open. As the nose elongates and the jaws enlarge, the face gains a distinctly human profile. The lips become clearly marked off from the skin of the face by the failure of the skin over the lips to thicken and cornify. The lips are smooth

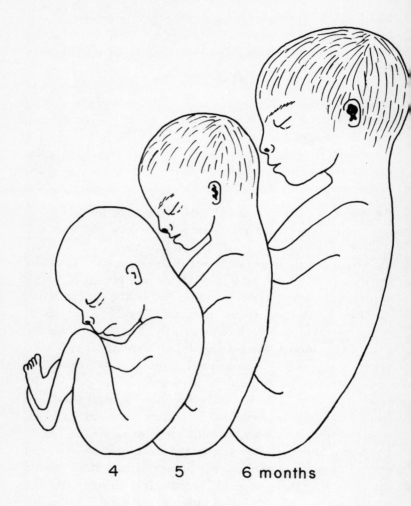

4   5   6 months

FIG. 21:

Development of the human fetus during the fourth, fifth, and sixth months of development. All of the fetuses are drawn to the same magnification, about one-half their actual size. (After Patten.)

100

and hairless along their outer edges, while the inner surface of the lips is covered by numerous small papillae. As a rule these lip papillae disappear before or shortly after birth.

Living creatures must be able to perceive changes in their environment if they are to adapt and survive. The human fetus lives in a dark, warm, moist, relatively uniform environment where there are few stimuli to arouse it from its nirvana-like existence. Yet the specialized sense organs that it will need after birth develop structurally and functionally before birth. Man traditionally believes that he has five senses—vision, hearing, smell, taste, and touch, with two or more special sense organs developed for each sense. Modern studies suggest that we have more than five senses, that we perceive and react to more kinds of stimuli from our environment than just light and sound waves, pressure and chemical changes. Heat and cold, tickle and deep pressure, pain and pleasure are some of our other sensory capacities. Not all the sensory organs reach functional maturity at the same time in fetal development, and probably none of them is fully developed before birth. But the six-month-old fetus is able to perceive and react to some sensory stimuli. This is not the same thing as saying that the fetus is conscious of sensation, that it knowingly recognizes the source of the stimulation or reacts purposefully to changes in its environment. Consciousness is a highly complex human activity that depends at least in part on the maturation of the brain, particularly of the cerebral hemispheres.

The eyes and internal ears are the most complex sense organs both in structure and in function. Though each of these sense organs begins its development before the end of the first month of life, their maturation progresses so slowly that it is doubtful whether they are functional before the end of the sixth month, and it is probable that they are only partially functional even after birth. The eyes arise in the fourth week of life as two symmetrical outpocketings from the embryonic neural tube. These two optic vesicles expand until they touch the surface skin, which they then induce to thicken to form two round lens plates. The outer ends of the optic vesicles become invaginated to form double-walled optic cups connected with the developing brain by a narrow stalk. All of this happens before the end of the first month of embryonic life.

During the following five months the optic cup and lens plate differentiate slowly to form the typical complex structures of the human eyeball. In the back of the eyeball the retina differentiates into rods and cones, the special sensory cells that are stimulated by light, and into nerve cells that are stimulated by the rods and cones to transmit nerve impulses to the developing brain through the fibers of the optic nerve. These optic nerve fibers grow into the embryonic brain from the eye, and spread through various parts of the brain until they reach a special region of the cerebral cortex, the visual center.

It is believed that these nerves develop their proper connections in the brain by the sixth month of fetal life, so that as soon as the sensitive rods and cones start to function, the eye and brain of the fetus are prepared to perceive light and to react to its stimulation. When the eyelids open late in the sixth month the fetus will react to a strong light stimulus with contraction of the pupils of the eyes, and the prematurely born infant gives evidence of being able to perceive light. At first the lens and pupil of the fetal eye are partially covered by a vascular membrane that would block out some of the light entering the eye, but these membranes are soon resorbed and the fetal eye is ready to function. The newborn infant has to learn through experience to focus his eyes and to use both eyes at the same time to look at a single image. It takes several months after birth for the infant to learn the complex reflex movements of the various eye muscles that are necessary for controlled binocular vision, but his eyes and brain are ready for this learning process by the seventh month of prenatal life.

Sound perception is made possible in man through the development of a complex three-part organ, the external, middle, and inner ear. The visible external ear is a flaring horn of cartilage and skin that funnels sound waves into the external ear canal. Both develop during the second month of embryonic life through conversion of the rudimentary first "gill" bars and clefts into the external ear and canal respectively. The gradual development of the external ear from the growth and fusion of six separate nodules of tissue is a highly variable process in the two-month embryo, resulting in the formation of widely different, distinctive kinds of external ears, one of the many characteristics that serve to make each fetus distinctively individual. The middle ear is a small hollow chamber in which three small ear bones develop. The middle ear chamber and bones, and the Eustachian tube that connects the chamber to the throat, develop in the human fetus through the remodeling of the embryonic first "gill" pouch and the tissues surrounding it. The ear bones transmit the pressure waves produced by sound from the ear drum that closes the external ear canal to the sensitive inner ear.

The inner ear is a double sensory organ that reacts not

only to sound waves but also to gravity, registering changes in the position of the entire body. In the fourth week of embryonic life a small round vesicle, the otic vesicle, develops on either side of the embryonic head near the expanding brain. This simple vesicle must undergo a complex sequence of changes in structure during the following five months of development before it can become functional. It differentiates into two distinct functional parts: a balance organ consisting of three slender semicircular canals; and a hearing organ, a coiled tube called the cochlea. The semicircular canals differentiate earliest, during the third month. Special sensory cells are stimulated when the fluid in the canals moves, whenever the head of the fetus moves, and special nerve fibers convey this stimulation to the brain. By the sixth month of life the fetus will try to turn the head or body whenever these nerves are stimulated, but the development of effective balancing reflexes depends on the complete development of the muscles of the body, the brain, and the experiences the infant has after he is removed from the supporting water-bath of amniotic fluid.

Hearing too is probably not completely developed by birth. The special sensory cells and nerves that react to sound waves develop slowly, and there is little evidence that the human fetus reacts to sound before the seventh month of development. But there is some evidence that during the last two months of intra-uterine life the fetus can be startled by sounds transmitted to it through the walls of the uterus and the mother's abdomen. It is intriguing to speculate that if the fetus does perceive sound during the last two months of its prenatal life, the sound that it hears is the continuous, rhythmic sound of his mother's heartbeat. In light of the clear evidence that the environment influences both the physical and psychic development of the human fetus, this prenatal presence of rhythmic sound as a part of the first home environment of man suggests that the human infant may be born with an inborn preference for rhythmic sounds as a memory of his prenatal life.

At birth the infant's sense of hearing seems to be deficient in most cases. The external ear canal would naturally be filled with fluid, since it is open to the amniotic sac throughout eight months of prenatal life. As this fluid drains out of the ear canal, the transmission of sound waves to the middle ear improves. The bones of the middle ear are not always freely movable at birth, but may be bound together by remnants of the tissues from which they developed. These remnants are resorbed or move out to the walls of the middle ear cavity, freeing the middle ear bones for flexible movement. The sensory cells and nerves of the inner ear are probably fully developed by the end of the sixth month of prenatal life, so the newborn infant is equipped to begin to learn auditory reactions as soon as the sound is properly transmitted to the inner ear. Newborn babies usually react to sudden loud sounds with a "startle reflex," a sudden contraction of many of the major muscles of the body. But the discrimination between different kinds of sounds that characterizes man's sense of hearing is probably developed only slowly during the first few months of independent life.

The sense of smell is an elusive, poorly understood ability that is difficult to test for in the fetus or infant. Little is known about when the fetus acquires the ability to distinguish odors. The sensory cells that react to odors have developed in the lining of the embryonic nasal cavities by the end of the second month. Experiments suggest that the eight-month fetus is able to perceive odors but the sense of smell is not well developed until some time after birth. The nostrils are plugged shut from the third through sixth months by an overgrowth of skin cells. When the nostrils are opened in the seventh month, amniotic fluid probably flows into the nasal cavities and bathes the olfactory lining.

After birth, when the amniotic fluid drains out of the mouth and nose, it is difficult to distinguish between the infant's reactions to odors and to taste. The lining of the mouth has numerous specialized taste buds that are stimulated by sweet, sour, or bitter chemicals. It is a curious fact that the human fetus has far more taste buds than does the infant or adult. At six months the linings of the lips, cheeks, palate, tongue, and throat are all covered with numerous taste buds, and the fetus will react to sweet substances with sucking movements and to bitter substances with protrusion of the tongue. During the last two months of prenatal life many of the fetal taste buds degenerate, and in the adult they remain only on the surface of the tongue, soft palate, and epiglottis. One might speculate that this early development of numerous taste buds is another example of the repetition in the development of the human fetus of the evolutionary history of the ancestors of man.

Touch is the first human sense to develop, and at birth it is probably the best-developed sense of the infant. Sensitivity to touch can be demonstrated only by the reactions of the fetus or infant to stimulation, and it is impossible to determine when the developing human becomes conscious of touch. By the end of the second month the embryo will react with movements to light stimulation of the skin around the mouth. During the third month the skin of the face, shoulders, and arms becomes sensitive. Soon the skin of the entire body becomes sensitive to touch and any stimulation may produce a reaction of the fetus. But again the ability to discriminate, to distinguish between light touch, strong pressure, and painful pressure, develops slowly and may not be present at birth. The conscious ability to locate the spot on the skin that is being stimulated is a still later development, probably not occurring until some time after birth, and in most humans this aspect of touch perception never becomes fully developed.

The human fetus lives in an environment where the amount and variety of sensory stimuli are probably low, so that although the sensory organs develop long before birth, it seems doubtful that they function very often during prenatal life. The uterus and the amniotic sac enclose the developing fetus in a warm, dark, quiet, uniform environment, where the changes that cause sensory stimulation are minimal. Up until the time when the birth contractions of the uterus begin to exert increasing pressure on the fetus, it seems probable that the human fetus has existed in a state of soothing tranquility. During the birth process, the sensory organs of the skin are subjected to increasing pressures, to dryness when the amniotic sac ruptures, and to cold when the infant leaves the birth canal. These stimuli all arouse a storm of sensory impulses in the sense organs, sensory nerves and brain. As a result of this flood of stimulation, a massive outflow of motor nerve impulses arouses the muscles to contraction, the chest muscles and diaphragm along with the other body muscles, and the infant takes his first breath and wails his first sound.

Now the sensory organs that cause the brain to stimulate the muscles to activity become necessary for survival. The fetus practiced sucking and swallowing within the uterus, when such movements were not necessary for getting food. The fetal tongue has been movable since the third month of development. Contractions of the abdominal muscles during fetal life often produce hiccups that are audible through the mother's abdominal wall. All of these reactions now become essential if the infant is to get and swallow his own food. By the end of the sixth month the fetus is prepared for this part of independent life, but rarely can such a fetus survive for very long. The best of medical care is unable to substitute for the immature brain of the six-month-old fetus, for the complex nervous system that must initiate, maintain, and control all of the activities of the human body in such a way that the steady state of balance necessary for life can be maintained.

CHAPTER 8

THE SEVENTH MONTH:

THE DOMINANT BRAIN

Now the waiting fetus crosses the unknown boundary between dependence and independence. For although he normally spends two more months within the secure haven of the uterus, he is nonetheless capable of independent life. If circumstances require it and the conditions of birth are favorable, the seven-month fetus is frequently able to survive premature birth.

One of the prime causes of the failure of younger fetuses to survive birth is believed to be the immaturity of the central nervous system, especially of those reflex centers in the brain that are concerned in maintaining constant, rhythmic breathing; in carrying out the sequence of muscular movements involved in swallowing; and in the intricate, delicately adjusted mechanism for maintaining body temperature. In the seven-month fetus the nervous system seems to be suffiicently developed to meet these demands of independent life.

The nervous system is the most complex system of the human body and this complexity is reflected in the fact that, although it is almost the first system to begin its development in the three-weeks-old embryo, it is almost the last system (except for the reproductive system) to reach functional maturity. The nervous system consists of a complex network of nerves connecting all of the organs of the body with the brain and spinal cord, the centralized clearing house for all the nerve impulses brought in from the sense organs and sent out to the muscles and glands. The entire nervous system has a common origin, the flat neural plate of the very young embryo, which during the fourth week of development rolls up to form a neural tube (Fig. 7). During the fifth week this neural tube grows and differentiates rapidly into the embryonic brain and spinal cord, from which nerves grow out to the skin, to all the organs of the body as they develop, and to the primitive muscle cells.

During the second and third months of life, as the various organs increase in complexity and shift in position, their nerves also increase in complexity and follow them to their new positions. Within the brain and spinal cord develop long connecting bundles of nerve fibers that serve to join all parts of the brain and cord with each other. Around the terminations of these internal nerve tracts, and around the nerves entering or leaving the brain or cord, large aggregations of nerve cells develop and give rise to still more connecting tracts. Gradually the external nerves and the internal tracts become functional, with the oldest nerve cells and fibers, oldest both in the development of the embryo and in the evolutionary history of mankind, beginning to function first and the newer, later formed tracts becoming functional later in fetal life or in life after birth.

The brain is the largest organ of the embryonic body during the second month of life (Fig. 22). As the fetus grows it forms a progressively smaller part of the total

110

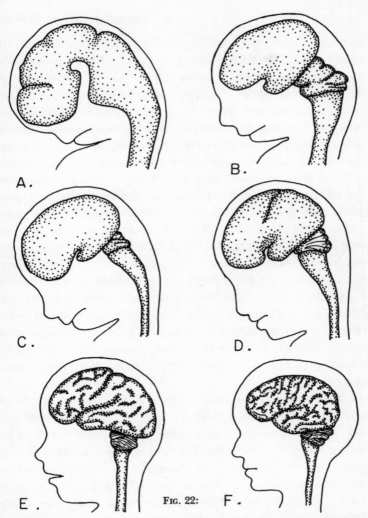

A.

B.

C.

D.

E.

Fig. 22:

F.

Diagrams showing the development of the brain in the human embryo, fetus and adult. The heads of the embryo at two months (A), three months (B), four months (C), six months (D), nine months (E) and the adult (F) are drawn at the same size to show the relative decrease in the portion of the head that is occupied by the brain. The cerebral hemispheres increase progressively in size relative to the rest of the brain. From six months on, the surface of the cerebral hemisphere is further increased by folding of the wall into ridges and grooves. (After Patten.)

body size and after birth it continues to decrease in relative size. It forms ten per cent of the total body weight in the newborn infant, but only two per cent of the total body weight of the adult. Within the brain the slowest but greatest growth occurs in the cerebral hemispheres, the most distinctive, elaborately developed organ of the human body, the prime factor in man's dominance over other animals. At two months the cerebral hemispheres are two small, thin-walled sacs outpocketed from the apex of the brain. During succeeding months of prenatal and postnatal life the cerebral hemispheres grow more rapidly than the rest of the brain, progressively overlapping and burying the other, older parts of the brain. Highly specialized nerve cells migrate out to the surface of the hemispheres to form the cerebral cortex, the highest controlling, integrating center of the human nervous system. The amount of cerebral cortex is continuously increased from six months on by the folding of the cortex into numerous ridges and grooves, forming the distinctive convolutions of "grey matter" that characterize the human cerebrum.

The nerve cells, fibers, and tracts begin to function only gradually, and it is quite likely that all of them are not fully functional until some years after birth. The first elements to become functional are the nerves that stimulate the muscles, causing some of them to contract early in the third month of prenatal life. The sensory nerves from the face become functional, and then stimulation of the face will cause reflex contractions of the shoulder, arm, and back muscles. Gradually as more and more nerves and nerve tracts within the brain and spinal cord begin to assume their typical functions, more areas of the fetal body become sensitive, more muscles of the

112

body wall and digestive tract contract and glandular secretions begin. Gradually the brain takes over its complex tasks of controlling and integrating the functions of all of the organs of the body, and the human fetus begins to acquire the behavior patterns that will characterize him throughout his entire life. Man learns by experience what kinds of behavior promote survival and well-being, even before birth. After birth this process of functional maturation of the nervous system continues as the individual continues to learn, unconsciously or consciously, the behavior patterns that he needs for successful independent life.

Survival of birth, when the human fetus is separated from his source of food, water, and oxygen through the placenta, depends primarily on his ability to start and maintain regular, continuous breathing. Most of the other essential functions of the human body have been carried on by the fetus within the uterus. The heart has been beating and circulating blood throughout the body ever since the end of the first month of life. The fetus has been swallowing amniotic fluid, digesting and absorbing some of its contents, since the fourth month. The kidneys have been excreting urine since the third month. Although some movements of the chest wall and diaphragm may occur before birth, these serve only to draw amniotic fluid into the lungs.

The lungs themselves are poorly developed before the seventh month of fetal life. The two lung buds that formed late in the first month grow slowly, branching repeatedly to form successive generations of the tubular bronchial trees that must eventually carry air from the throat and trachea to the terminal air sacs in the lungs, where oxygen can diffuse into the blood and carbon dioxide diffuse out into the air sacs. By seven months only two thirds of the bronchial tubes and air sacs have been formed. By nine months three fourths of the two lungs have developed. Not until the middle of childhood will the lungs be fully developed. But by the seventh month of prenatal life enough air sacs have developed to provide the growing fetus with the oxygen needed for life. The muscles of the chest wall and diaphragm necessary for inhaling and exhaling are fully functional. When the reflex nerve arcs necessary for controlling their rhythmic contraction and relaxation mature within the brain, the fetus is ready to start regular breathing.

The time when the human fetus can live independently does not arrive at a crucial moment that is the same for every man. The ability of each individual to survive birth depends on a great many variables—his size, age, degree of developmental maturity, the severity of the events that occur to him during the birth process, and the nature of the special care that he receives after birth. As our knowledge of the development and maturation of the human fetus has accumulated, and our understanding of the handicaps of the premature infant has increased, the chances for survival of the prematurely born infant have improved.

Normally the human fetus spends about thirty-eight weeks in the uterus (forty weeks of pregnancy), but some fetuses are able to survive birth after only two thirds of this time (about twenty-five weeks of life) have passed. At this time the fetus weighs about two pounds and is about thirteen inches long, although these measurements vary considerably depending on the heredity of the individual and his rate of growth within the uterus. The chances of such a young premature fetus surviving long enough after birth to complete his interrupted development are slim.

Every additional week that is spent in the uterus beyond this time increases the chances of the infant for survival. After thirty weeks of development, when most fetuses will weigh at least three pounds, the probability of survival increases rapidly. If the fetus spends at least thirty-six weeks within the uterus and reaches a weight of more than five pounds, he has about the same chance of surviving as does the fully mature thirty-eight-week-old fetus.

The handicaps of the premature fetus are numerous, and their severity depends on the degree of development and maturation of all of the organs of his body. His first problem is starting and maintaining constant, rhythmic breathing. The lungs are poorly developed, have fewer air sacs than at maturity, and have insufficient elastic tissue within their walls. The respiratory reflexes are weak, and breathing is frequently shallow and irregular.

His second problem is getting food and eliminating waste products. Although sucking and swallowing begin well before this time, the reflexes that control them are not mature and the premature infant has trouble coordinating sucking, tongue movements, swallowing and gagging. His stomach is small and will hold only a small amount of food without regurgitation. Peristalsis in the intestine is weak, and the plug of fetal feces, the meconium, may not be passed out of the body promptly. The liver and kidneys do not function well, even though they have been carrying out their essential functions in part for several months.

The third major problem for the premature infant is the maintenance of a constant body temperature. Because of his small size he has a high ratio of surface skin, where heat is lost, to internal volume, where heat is generated by cellular metabolism. Nerve control of the capillaries below the skin is poorly matured, so he may lose heat faster than his body creates it. He is likely to be less active in movement than is a full-term fetus, so his hands and feet become cold more easily.

The premature infant is handicapped not only by the fact that his various organs are not fully developed, but also by the fact that he has been separated from the rich and easy source of supplies from the placenta. The minerals that are needed by his rapidly growing bones are more richly available from the mother's blood than from the food he must digest and absorb for himself. He is highly susceptible to infection through his relatively thin, delicate skin and he has little ability within himself for forming the antibodies that can combat infection. During the last two months of normal prenatal life, the human fetus receives from his mother through the placenta many of the antibodies that she has developed against the various infections and diseases she has experienced in the course of her longer life. These maternal antibodies give the full-term infant considerable temporary immunity against the infections and diseases that may attack him.

At the end of the seventh month of life the human fetus is a red-skinned, wrinkled, wizened, old-looking human being, about three pounds in weight and about sixteen inches long. If born he will breathe, cry, and swallow. He is aware of the taste of food, for he will respond with specific facial expressions when sweet, sour, or bitter substances are placed on his tongue. He probably perceives the difference between light and dark, for he will turn his head away from a bright light. Best of all, he has a chance to survive in independent life.

CHAPTER 9

THE EIGHTH AND NINTH MONTHS:

INDEPENDENCE

NOW THE YOUNG HUMAN BEING, ready for birth, with all his essential organs able to function, spends two more months putting the finishing touches on his anatomy, improving his rather questionable beauty, and maturing those abilities necessary for independent life after birth. During each of these months he gains approximately two pounds in weight and two inches in height. Every extra day that he spends in the uterus, up to a certain optimum, improves his chance of surviving birth.

Anyone who has seen a prematurely born seven-month infant would agree that these last two months of development materially improve the appearance of the fetus. During these two months the fetus loses the wizened, senile appearance of the seven-month fetus and gradually attains the more acceptable appearance of a human infant. During the first seven months of life little fat is deposited anywhere in the fetal body, since all of the food materials taken in through the placenta are used to promote growth and development of the various organs. But during the last two months of normal intra-uterine life enough extra food becomes available for some of it to be stored in the tissues of the fetus as fat deposits. A blanket of fat is formed in the connective tissues immediately under the fetal skin, smoothing out the wrinkles in the skin, hiding the underlying bones and muscles, and rounding out the contours of the fetal body. The dull red color of the skin fades gradually to a more delicate flesh pink. Pigmentation of the skin is very slight, so even the offspring of colored races are relatively light-skinned at birth. The lanugo coat of fine, downy hair that earlier covered the skin usually disappears during the eighth and ninth months from all regions of the body except perhaps the shoulders and back. Part of the body, particularly the back, is still covered with the cheesy vernix caseosa, although the amount of this pasty covering of the skin varies greatly in different fetuses. The nails grow rapidly and at birth may project beyond the tips of the fingers and toes.

Within the mouth the lips lose the velvety papillae they had earlier, and the taste buds that covered the entire mouth lining begin to degenerate so that the newborn infant has fewer taste buds than did the six-month fetus. The gums acquire a peculiar ridging and grooving that is occasionally so marked as to give the appearance of teeth. It is probable that many of the tales of babies born with teeth already erupted are based on a false interpretation of these ridges on the gums.

The twenty teeth that will begin to erupt through the gums six months after birth are developing rapidly, buried down within the gum tissue. The enamel crowns of these first teeth are now being formed, and the full-term fetus has a great advantage over the premature fetus in being able to get the minerals needed for enamel formation from the mother through the placenta. Any disturbance in the health of either the mother or the fetus is likely to affect enamel formation and give rise to abnormal or incomplete enamel in the baby teeth. The roots of the teeth are only beginning to grow at this time, but they will grow rapidly in the following six months, leading eventually to the eruption of the teeth through the overlying gums. Thirty of the permanent teeth, which will not be fully formed until six to twenty years after birth, have begun to develop. New tooth buds grow from the tongue side of each of the original tooth buds, push down alongside the developing baby teeth, and form enamel cups over dental papillae for the permanent teeth. Calcification and enamel formation in these teeth do not occur until after birth.

The internal organs continue to develop and mature. The lungs undergo further branching of the bronchiole tree and more air sacs form, so that the fetal lung is considerably more adequate by the end of nine months than it was after seven months. Peristalsis becomes stronger and more dependable in the digestive tract. New kidney tubules are formed and the first formed tubules degenerate. By birth the functions of the kidney have improved enough so that the fetus is able to excrete urine adequately without wasting the precious salts that the seven-month kidney was unable to resorb properly. But probably the greatest advantage that the nine-month fetus has over the seven-month fetus lies in the maturation of the nervous system, especially of the reflex patterns that control breathing, sucking, swallowing, peristalsis, defecation, urination and heat loss. Even though the human fetus can get through these two months of life outside of the uterus, it is still a considerable advantage if they can be spent within the warm, nurturing environment of the uterus.

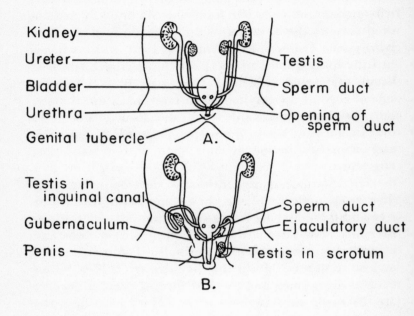

Kidney
Ureter
Bladder
Urethra
Genital tubercle

Testis
Sperm duct
Opening of
sperm duct

A.

Testis in
inguinal canal
Gubernaculum
Penis

Sperm duct
Ejaculatory duct
Testis in scrotum

B.

FIG. 23:

Diagrams of the male reproductive organs in the third month (A) and
in the seventh and eighth months (B) of prenatal life. The testes lie at
the level of the kidneys in the third month, and are connected to the
urethra by the sperm duct. At the beginning of the seventh month the
testes lie on the floor of the pelvic cavity, attached to the scrotal sac by
a ligament, the gubernaculum (left side of B). By the end of the eighth
month the testes have descended into the scrotal sac (right side of B).
The upper end of the sperm duct remains attached to the testis throughout this process, so after the testis has moved into the scrotum, the sperm
duct runs from the scrotum up into the pelvic cavity, where it loops
over the ureter before it enters the urethra.

120

The reproductive organs of both the male and female fetus undergo considerable development during the last two months of prenatal life. In the male the basic architecture of the testis is well established by the fifth month when the sex cords, formed in the third month, differentiate into distinct looped cords. These cords connect with the old mesonephric tubules that join the testis to the old mesonephric duct, which now becomes the vas deferens or sperm duct. By the seventh month the sex cords have become tubules with a central cavity that connects with the cavity of the sperm duct, and with walls made up of prospective sperm cells. A few of the larger cells begin to undergo the process of differentiation that in the adult leads to the formation of sperm, but these earliest sex cells degenerate by birth or soon after. Most of the immature sex cells remain quiescent in the walls of the testis tubules throughout childhood, and begin to differentiate into sperm cells only at puberty.

The position of the testes in the fetal body changes rapidly during the last third of prenatal life (Fig. 23). Originally the testes developed at the same level of the body as the stomach. In the following months the testes gradually move backward, toward and into the growing pelvic region. By the beginning of the seventh month they lie on the floor of the pelvic cavity, near the place where the scrotal sacs developed in the fourth month. It was pointed out earlier that the scrotal sacs are outpocketings of the entire body wall—skin, muscle layer, and the smooth peritoneal lining of the central body cavity. The internal space within the scrotal sacs is thus continuous with the cavity of the pelvis. During the seventh month the testes slide out of the pelvic cavity and into these scrotal sacs.

Here the testes usually lie at birth, and here they

121

should remain throughout life. This descent of the testes, which is permanent in man and some animals but occurs only during the breeding season in others, is a curious phenomenon. It seems to be a necessary preliminary to the formation of fertile sperm in the testes of man, for if this descent is incomplete, leaving the testes in the pelvis or inguinal canal, the man is usually sterile. After the descent of the testes is completed, the upper end of the narrow inguinal canal, which connects the scrotal sacs with the pelvic cavity, usually closes. But in about half of all male infants this closure is incomplete until after birth. In most males the place where the inguinal canal closed remains throughout life as a weak point in the abdominal wall, the source of the rupture and hernia that frequently occur in males.

The female reproductive organs develop more slowly than the male organs, but during the last two months of intra-uterine life the female sex hormones being secreted by the mother and by the placenta stimulate rapid development of the reproductive organs in the female fetus. Within the ovary some follicles containing maturing egg cells develop during the last two months of prenatal life. But once the infant is born and removed from the influence of the maternal and placental sex hormones, these first follicles degenerate and the ovary returns to a quiescent state until puberty begins. It has been claimed by some scientists that all of the prospective egg cells that will mature during the adult life of the woman are present and already formed within the fetal ovary. Others dispute this claim and say that the ova that mature into eggs during adult life are new descendants of undifferentiated cells of the fetal ovary. This argument is of more than theoretical importance, since if the future egg cells are formed in the fetal ovary, then they are subject to any deleterious influences that may occur during prenatal life. If, on the other hand, new egg cells can be developed in the mature ovary, then it becomes important for the fertility of the woman that some of the ovary be left intact in surgical operations.

The ovaries undergo a limited descent comparable to the descent of the testes, but since no scrotal sacs are formed in the female fetus, this descent stops when the ovaries reach the back wall of the pelvic cavity. The sex ducts of the female, formed from the two Mullerian ducts that fuse in the midline at their lower ends, differentiate into the two Fallopian tubes, the single uterus and vagina. The opening of the vagina into the vestibule is blocked during development by a solid plug of cells, and remnants of this plug remain after birth as the hymen, a more or less incomplete membrane over the outlet of the vagina. The fetal uterus enlarges rapidly during the last two months of intra-uterine life, probably under the influence of the mother's sex hormones. Frequently the lining of the fetal uterus will become temporarily engorged with blood in a manner that resembles the premenstrual thickening of the endometrium in the adult uterus. After birth, when the maternal sex hormones are no longer affecting the female infant, the uterus shrinks to its typical small, infantile size and remains small until puberty is reached.

The maternal and placental sex hormones also stimulate the rapid development of the mammary glands of the fetus during the last two months of development. Mammary glands arise as modified sweat glands in the pectoral skin of embryos of both sexes during the second month. Although normally only one pair of mammary glands form in humans, sometimes extra glands develop on the chest, abdominal, or pelvic walls. The mammary glands develop slowly in fetuses of both sexes, and at birth the small mammae and their nipples are the same in both male and female infants. The sex hormones of the mother and the placenta frequently stimulate the mammary glands of both male and female newborn infants to secrete a thin watery milk, called "witches'-milk," during the first few days after birth. But then the mammary glands return to a quiescent state and no further development occurs until puberty.

The advantages that the full-term infant has over the prematurely born infant come from the extra time that the fetus is supported by the placenta. After the placenta was established in the second month of pregnancy through the exuberant growth of the trophoblast villi invading, destroying, and absorbing the tissues of the uterine lining, the growth of the placenta gradually slows down. During the first four months of pregnancy the placenta is larger than the fetus, but during the last five months the fetus grows faster than the placenta.

At the end of pregnancy the human placenta is a flattened disc of spongy tissue, about six to eight inches in diameter and one inch thick. When it is removed from the uterus as part of the after-birth, it is found to weigh about one to two pounds. While it is embedded in the uterine wall, the spaces within its spongy tissues are filled with maternal blood that is forced into the spaces from the maternal uterine arteries and drained out of them through the uterine veins. Within the placental spaces, the maternal blood flows slowly past the trophoblastic villi that form the fetal part of the placenta. Within these dangling villi lie branches of the fetal umbilical blood vessels through which flows the fetal blood. Between the

124

maternal and fetal blood lies the placental barrier, a layer of fetal tissues formed from the trophoblast of the young embryo and the lining of the fetal blood vessels.

Through this placental barrier pass all of the substances—food, water, oxygen, hormones, minerals, vitamins—that the mother supplies to the fetus, and also all of the waste products and hormones that pass from the fetus to the mother. The welfare of both the mother and the fetus depends on the efficiency of this placental barrier. The rate of transfer of substances from the mother to the fetus increases during the course of pregnancy, thus meeting the constantly increasing demands of the rapidly growing fetus. Studies of the physiology of the placenta suggest that this rate of transfer reaches a peak of efficiency at about thirty-four to thirty-five weeks of pregnancy and then begins to decrease.

During the last month of pregnancy the placenta begins to show signs of ageing. Its efficiency as a source of food for the fetus decreases and some parts of the placenta begin to degenerate. When the placental barrier is thus destroyed, substances that probably do not pass through the placenta easily during earlier stages begin to be exchanged between mother and fetus. Blood cells of the mother may appear in the fetal blood stream, and fetal blood cells cross over into the maternal blood stream. These two types of blood cells may be incompatible with each other, since the fetus has inherited his blood genes from the father as well as the mother. The fetal blood cells may then provoke the formation of antibodies against its cells in the mother's blood. Such antibodies may pass back through the placenta into the fetal blood stream, where they attack and destroy the fetal blood cells.

The fetus has little ability to form antibodies for itself,

so it is often fortunate that maternal antibodies can and do pass through the placenta into the fetus. Whatever antibodies the mother may have acquired, during the course of her life, against the various diseases she has experienced, or against which she has been inoculated, will pass into the fetal blood stream and confer a temporary, passive immunity against these diseases on the fetus. So the human infant is usually immune against many diseases during the crucial first few months of his life after birth, when his own ability to form antibodies is only gradually developing. Unfortunately viruses and bacteria can also pass through the placenta in some cases and infect the defenseless fetus with the same diseases that his mother is experiencing.

Now that the nine months of intra-uterine life are almost completed and the fetus is soon to be expelled from the uterus, it is of some importance that we should note the position and surroundings of the fetus. This invader, who almost nine months earlier dug a nest for itself within the wall of the uterus, has now not only usurped the entire uterine cavity for its home but has forced an enormous enlargement of this accommodating maternal organ. The enlarging uterus necessarily occupies a constantly increasing portion of the mother's abdominal cavity, forcing a protrusion of the abdominal wall as the apex of the uterus moves up toward the diaphragm (Fig. 24). Normally lying entirely in the pelvis, the uterus expands during pregnancy to the level of the mother's navel during the first four months and almost to the level of the diaphragm by the end of the eighth month. Then as the mature fetus settles down toward the mouth of the uterus, the apex of the uterus drops slightly.

Within the uterus the fetus may occupy any possible

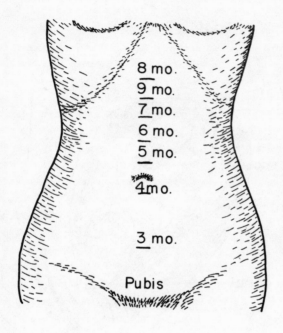

8 mo.
9 mo.
7 mo.
6 mo.
5 mo.

4 mo.

3 mo.

Pubis

FIG. 24:

Torso of a pregnant woman showing the approximate height of the uterus in each month of pregnancy. Maximum height is reached early in the ninth month, after which the fetus drops into the lower part of the uterus and the apex of the uterus falls slightly.

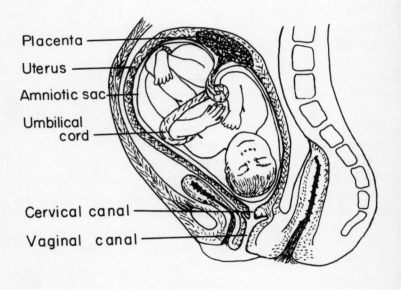

Placenta

Uterus

Amniotic sac

Umbilical cord

Cervical canal

Vaginal canal

Fig. 25:

The mature fetus within the uterus. The location of the placenta and the position of the fetus are variable in individual cases, but this shows the most common position of both.

128

position, but most frequently it lies with its head down and rump up, with its back parallel with the mother's back (Fig. 25). The umbilical cord, which is usually as long as the fetus itself (about twenty inches), follows a coiled and variable course from the future navel of the fetus to the middle of the placenta. Through this cord run three large fetal blood vessels, one umbilical vein and two umbilical arteries. The blood of the fetus is pumped out to the placenta through these arteries, flows slowly through the placenta, and is returned to the fetus through the vein. The fetus floats in about one quart of watery amniotic fluid. The amniotic sac holding this fluid has now fused with the lining of the uterus to a large extent. The outlet to the uterus, the cervical canal, is usually closed by a thick mucus plug, held in place by the strong circular muscles that surround the cervix. The birth canal consists of the cervical canal and the vagina, which opens into the vestibule lying between the mother's labia.

The fully mature fetus differs from the newborn infant in two important respects: the fact that it is attached to the placenta by the umbilical cord through which its blood is being circulated; and the fact that its lungs are not being used in breathing. The circulation of the fetal blood through the placenta is the most important part of the fetal circulation since the survival of the fetus depends on this circulation, which must continue until the infant has started to breathe for itself. During fetal life, when the lungs are not being used, most of the fetal blood by-passes the useless lungs by flowing from the right half of the divided heart, where the pulmonary vessel arises, directly into the left half of the heart. This is made possible by the foramen ovale, the hole left in the dividing partition of the atria when it developed during the second month of life. In addition, the lung circulation is further by-passed by a special blood vessel, the ductus arteriosus, that connects the pulmonary aorta with the dorsal aorta. So some of the fetal blood that does not cross through the foramen ovale can still by-pass the useless lungs. When the newborn infant starts to breathe, both of these fetal by-pass routes must be closed and all of the fetal blood must be forced to flow through the lungs. During the birth process or soon after, the placenta is torn loose from its intimate fusion with the wall of the mother's uterus, and the umbilical circulation becomes useless to the newborn infant. It is obvious that at the time of birth, as soon as the infant breathes effectively and the placenta is torn from the uterine wall, something will have to be done about these two special aspects of the fetal circulation.

Even now a forewarning of the coming birth, in fact of the necessity for birth, can be read in the placenta, for the placenta seems to be ageing. Patches of degeneration appear; islands of tough fibrous connective tissue may render parts of the placenta useless; massive blood clots may form in some spots, halting the flow of the mother's blood through these regions. These changes suggest that the placenta is approaching the end of its functional ability, and when the placenta ceases to function the fetus must at once take over the job of fully supporting and protecting its own tissues and organs. This can be accomplished only in the outer world, which the human infant must now enter.

CHAPTER 10

EXODUS

BIRTH IS THE TIME of exodus from the uterus, the beginning of independent life. The exact time when birth occurs varies in the lives of different individuals. The average length of human pregnancy is about two hundred and eighty days from the onset of the last true menstrual period, or about nine months and ten days. Although no more than ten per cent of all human infants are born on the two hundred and eightieth day, seventy-five per cent are born within two weeks of that day. In terms of the individual life of the infant from fertilization to birth, the length of prenatal life is usually about two hundred and sixty-six days, although this may vary from two hundred and fifty to three hundred days and still be counted as a normal period of development.

Just what specific event, or events, initiates the normal birth process remains unknown in spite of extensive medical studies. For some weeks previous to birth, slow, rhythmic muscular contractions, similar to those that cause "labor pains," occur in a mild, intermittent fashion in the pregnant uterus. Why the uterus, after withstanding this long period of futile contractions, is suddenly thrown into powerful, compulsive muscular contractions that expel the fetus from the uterus remains the final mystery of our prenatal life. It is quite probable that the birth process is not initiated solely within the uterus, but occurs as a complex reaction of the mother's entire body. It is known that hormones from the mother's endocrine glands, particularly from the pituitary gland, act to provoke and control the contractions of the powerful uterine muscles.

There is nothing sacrosanct about the proverbial nine months and ten days that are allotted as the expected duration of pregnancy. The fact that there is wide variation in the time of normal births, together with the fact that seven-month-old fetuses are able to survive birth, suggests that birth is not a critical moment in man's life span, not a sharply delimited end of one period of life and the beginning of another, but rather a period of transition, of change in environment, occurring at some point during the continuous growth and development of the human body.

This continuous process of growth can be summarized in a schedule showing the approximate age, size, and weight of the human fetus during the successive months of the mother's pregnancy. The sizes and weights given in such a table are only rough approximations since the growth of each individual fetus varies with his heredity,

Month of pregnancy	Days of pregnancy	Age of fetus in weeks	Weight of fetus	Length of fetus
1	1 — 31	2+		
2	32 — 63	7		
3	64 — 95	11½	½ ounce	2½ inches
4	96 — 126	16	¼ pound	5 inches
5	127 — 157	20½	1 pound	10 inches
6	158 — 189	25	2 pounds	13 inches
7	190 — 221	29½	3 pounds	16 inches
8	222 — 252	34	5 pounds	18 inches
9	253 — 283	38	7 pounds	20 inches

the efficiency of his placenta, and with whether or not he is alone in the uterus.

The weight of the human infant at the time of normal birth may vary from six and one half to nine pounds. The most critical aspect of his size is not his weight or length, but the size of his head. In fact it seems quite likely that the time of birth in man has been determined, during the process of the evolution of the human species, by the rate of growth of the fetal head. At birth the fetus must pass through the rigid bony pelvic girdle of his mother, and the size of the fetal head must not be greater than the size of the outlet through the maternal pelvis. The diameter of the pelvic outlet varies in different women but on the average it is about four to six inches wide in its narrowest part. The head of the full-term human fetus is usually about four to five inches wide at its widest part, and about fourteen inches in circumference. If the size of the fetal head is larger than the size of the pelvic outlet of the mother, the bones of the fetal skull will be pushed together and the underlying brain will be squeezed during the passage of the fetal head through the birth canal. The head and brain of the human infant continue to grow rapidly during the first months after birth. So the time when birth must occur for the safety of the human infant lies in a fairly narrow range between the time when the various organs become functionally competent and the time when the head becomes too large to pass safely through the pelvis.

Birth (or in medical terms parturition) is the process of expelling the fetus and all of its adjuncts—the placenta, amniotic sac and fluid, from the uterus. It is brought about through the involuntary, rhythmic, powerful contractions of the layers of intertwining muscles forming the walls of the uterus. Voluntary contractions of the muscles of the abdominal wall and diaphragm may aid in this process by exerting extra pressure on the outside of the uterus. The uterine contractions compress the contents of the uterus and force the fetus against the weakest part of the uterine wall, the cervical opening (Fig. 25).

This pressure stretches the outlet of the uterus, permitting the gradual passage of the fetus into and through the birth canal and then out of the vagina into the external world. It is not our purpose to relate here the important and complex obstetrical side of this story, the many events and sensations that form the mother's part of the birth process. Such events are the concern of the preceding generation. This tale deals only with the life processes of the new human being who is being born.

The journey through the narrow confines of the birth canal, with or without external aid, is frequently arduous and hazardous for the infant. One writer has suggested that this short journey through the four inches of the birth canal is probably the most dangerous journey made by any individual during life. The infant may be bruised or even have bones broken. The thin, loosely joined bones of the skull may be pressed into distorted shapes or positions. The pressures exerted by the uterine contractions slow down the heartbeat and blood circulation of the infant, causing temporary starvation of his tissues for oxygen and food. But if he was endowed at fertilization with sufficient viability, if the course of his development has been normal, and if the birth passageways are normal in size, the infant usually survives this journey without serious mishap.

Some scientists have suggested that the birth process

produces invisible but permanent damage to the psychic nature of the human being. Psychiatrists speak of the "birth trauma" as an influential factor in the nature of human life. They point out that birth involves a cataclysmic change in the environment and mode of living of the human infant, that it causes a sudden loss of the security and freedom from effort that characterize prenatal life. They suggest that at this time fear and anxiety become part of the human psyche, so that the future life of the individual is plagued by unconscious memories of his tranquil prenatal life and his stormy entrance into independent life.

It must be recalled that within the uterus the fetus was enclosed in a fluid-filled sac, the amnion. At some stage in the birth process, usually before the fetus leaves the uterus, this sac ruptures and "the waters" ·escape through the birth canal. Usually the amniotic sac ruptures in such a way that the fetus passes through the hole formed, leaving the entire amniotic sac within the uterus. Occasionally part of the sac will remain around the fetus as he passes through the birth canal, to appear as a translucent membrane wrapped around the infant. Such an infant is said to have been born with a veil, and in medieval times this was believed to be a sign of good luck, of superior ability, or even of "second sight" for the fortunate child.

As soon as the infant is born he usually gasps, fills his lungs with air, and utters his first bleating cry. Normally the storm of stimuli that entrance into the external world inflicts on his skin, sensory organs, nerves and brain causes this first gasp and cry. If this does not occur, the same result can be achieved by holding the newborn infant up by his heels and lightly spanking him. The infant is still connected with the placenta lodged within the uterus, so once he has started breathing he gets little further attention until the placenta, the amniotic sac, and most of the lining of the uterus are removed from the uterus as the after-birth.

Usually the ageing placenta is loosened from the uterine wall during the strong contractions of the uterine muscles, and is readily forced or drawn out of the uterus. This of course at once destroys the close relation between the fetal and maternal blood streams, and the infant is now on his own. The umbilical blood vessels, which attach the infant to the placenta through the umbilical cord, pulsate for a short time as the blood is forced out to the placenta and returned to the infant's body. It is important that the infant should remain connected with the placenta for a short time so that the large amount of fetal blood that was in the placenta at the time of birth can be returned to the infant's body through the umbilical vein. The moist, fragile tissue of the umbilical cord dries and shrivels fairly rapidly, constricting the umbilical blood vessels and gradually decreasing the flow of blood to the placenta. The umbilical cord is then tied off and cut a short distance from the infant's body. This stump soon degenerates but its scar, the defect in the abdominal wall caused by the attachment of the cord to the fetus, remains throughout life as the navel—a permanent reminder of our once parasitic mode of living.

The newborn infant is by no means a finished and perfect human being. Several immediate adjustments are required by the change from intra-uterine to independent life. Various conditions or events occur that are peculiar to the newborn infant, and many of his organs are still incomplete in form or function.

The most dramatic event that occurs at birth is the first cry of the infant, signalling the initial passage of air into and out of the lungs. The lungs at birth are relatively small, compact masses of seemingly dense tissue. The first few breaths of the infant expand the lungs until they fill all of the available space within the chest cavity. As the numerous air sacs become filled with air, the lungs become light and spongy in texture. New air sacs continue to be formed throughout early childhood, and even those already formed at birth do not function perfectly until several days of regular breathing have passed. The small amount of amniotic fluid that was drawn into the fetal lungs by abortive breathing movements of the fetal chest wall is rapidly absorbed into the blood capillaries of the lungs during the first few days after birth.

The onset of breathing, together with the severing of the circulation to the placenta when the umbilical cord is cut, requires and produces profound changes in the infant's circulatory system. The blood, which in the fetus was shunted away from the inactive lungs, is now drawn in constantly increasing amounts through the lungs. The opening in the partition between the two atria, which allowed the blood to by-pass the lungs in the fetus, is closed by a flap-like valve that slams the door shut on the foramen ovale. This valve adheres to the wall of the atrial septum and gradually the hole is closed permanently by the growth of fibers across the fetal opening. This hole in the heart septum is not closed completely and permanently until about six to eight weeks after birth, and in some infants it never closes entirely. At the same time the blood vessel that shunted some of the fetal blood from the pulmonary artery directly into the dorsal aorta constricts to a narrow channel, preventing the infant's blood from by-passing the lungs. This vessel soon degenerates into a solid cord of tough tissue that remains throughout life as a reminder of the fetal circulatory route. When these two fetal by-pass routes have been closed, all of the infant's blood circulates through the lungs, where it absorbs oxygen from the inhaled air and gives off carbon dioxide into the exhaled air.

Even more drastic and immediate changes occur in the placental circulation. Shortly before birth the vessels to and from the placenta show signs of regression, and as soon as the umbilical cord is tied and cut, circulation through these vessels stops at once. The umbilical arteries and vein gradually degenerate into fibrous cords of tissue that remain on the inner surface of the abdominal wall as additional reminders of our early dependence on the placenta.

These birth changes pose critical problems for the infant's heart. As the placental circulation closes, the great volume of blood that flows through the placenta in fetal life is suddenly added to the infant's body circulation. Any rise in blood volume always causes a rise in blood pressure, forcing the heart to contract more strongly to circulate the blood. As the blood pressure rises after birth, the rate of the heartbeat, which had slowed down considerably during the birth process, speeds up. As the lungs are inflated, the rich network of blood capillaries that lie around the air sacs in the lungs opens up, and the heart must then begin to pump blood through the lungs as well as through the body circulation. In the fetus the right half of the heart was larger and stronger than the left half, since it received and pumped out the large amount of blood coming from the placenta. During the first two weeks of postnatal life the left half of the heart enlarges, its muscular wall thickens, and the left ventricle becomes the main propulsive part of the heart.

Shortly after the shock of birth has worn off, the infant excretes the small amount of urine that had collected in the bladder. The dark green meconium that had accumulated in the fetal intestines during the second half of development is passed out of the anus. All of the fetal meconium is usually defecated during the first four days after birth. After that time the infant passes only the light-colored feces that are formed as the residue from its milk diet. One peculiarity of the newborn infant is the fact that its intestines and their contents are completely sterile. The elaborate bacterial population present in the intestines of all independent human beings appears only after birth, when the infant becomes infected from the external environment. Not uncommonly the secretion of bile from the liver is disturbed during the birth process, and a temporary jaundice may give a faint yellowish tinge to the skin and the whites of the eyes.

A puzzling, drastic change occurs in the adrenal glands of the newborn infant. The two adrenal glands are small oval endocrine glands that lie above the kidneys. They secrete several important hormones both before and after birth. During prenatal life the adrenal cortex is much larger in proportion to the total size of the fetal body than it is in the child or the adult. Just before birth and during the first few weeks after birth the adrenal cortex shrinks in size, as a result of the rapid degeneration of the cells that were secreting its hormones into the fetal body. Then gradually during childhood a new permanent adrenal cortex develops from the thin layer of tissue that did not degenerate. At present scientists are unable to

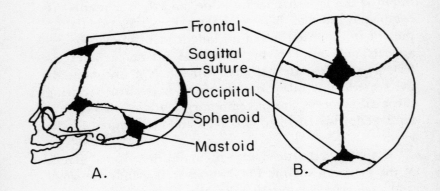

Frontal
Sagittal
suture
Occipital
Sphenoid
Mastoid

A.

B.

FIG. 26:

Skull of the newborn infant, showing the fontanelles and sutures (black) between the skull bones (white).
A. Side view.
B. Top view.

140

explain either the great growth of the adrenal cortex before birth or its shrinkage after birth.

Many of the infant's organs are not completely developed at birth. The most obvious example is the skull (Fig. 26). The roofing bones of the skull are not only thin, but they are incompletely joined together. Four distinct pairs of flat bones are involved in making the roof of the skull, and at the angles between successive pairs there are wide spaces where no bone has yet been formed. There are six of these "soft spots" or fontanelles on the newborn infant's head: one in the top middle, a short distance behind the forehead; the second also in the middle, near the back of the head; and two on each side of the head, one at the temple and one behind the ear. In addition there are still narrow lines of separation between adjacent edges of all the skull bones. The fontanelles are largely covered during the first three years of life, but the various bones do not fuse to form a unified skull until the brain and head have reached adult size.

The deposition of fat under the skin continues uninterrupted if the infant's diet is adequate. Such fat formation serves to improve still more the contours of the body and to hasten the fading of the pink color of the skin. Pigmentation of the skin starts soon after birth, so infants of dark-skinned ancestry darken appreciably during the first two months. Neither tear glands nor salivary glands are completely developed at birth. The newborn infant cries without tears, and his saliva does not acquire its full starch-digesting powers until near weaning time.

In the kidney additional tubules must still be formed. The liver is still too large in proportion to the other organs of the abdominal cavity. The stomach is small, capable of holding only a few fluid ounces without distension. The pyloric sphincter, which guards the outlet of the stomach into the intestine, is not reliable, so regurgitation of food from either the stomach or intestine is liable to occur easily. The eyes, although sensitive to light, have not yet acquired the power of focusing on one point, so the newborn infant may be temporarily crosseyed. Most important of all of these deficiencies, the great bundles of nerve fibers that connect the various parts of the brain with each other and with all parts of the body are not fully developed, structurally or functionally. So although the newborn infant is equipped to begin to learn useful behavior patterns, he is by no means prepared to learn all of the various activities possible for the mature human being.

Thus the first nine months of human life are completed. The new human being has passed through two epochs of his life—the embryonic and the fetal. He has grown enormously in size and complexity during his nine months of parasitic life within his mother. The manifold changes occurring during this period form the first personal history of each member of the human race. It is the one phase of life that we all have in common, since it is essentially the same for all men. But even here it cannot rightly be claimed that all men are created equal, for behind every generation lies the preceding generation, and the hereditary traits of structure and function with which each man is endowed at fertilization make his life individual and characteristic, even during these first nine months.

CHAPTER 11

TWINS AND VARIATIONS

THE HUMAN BODY develops through a sequence of changes that are basically the same for all men. Most human infants at birth resemble other newborn infants so closely that it is frequently difficult for even the parents to recognize their own child when he is compared with other newborn infants. But there are many differences between infants, some being specific individual traits, such as fingerprints, footprints, shape of the ears, blood type, and other genetically determined traits. Other differences may be the result of variations in the developmental processes. These variations range all the way from slight differences in size or degree of maturity of specific organs, through various kinds of aberrant development, to severe abnormalities of organs or whole regions of the body. It is quite possible for the human embryo or fetus to survive through the nine months of prenatal life in spite of slight or serious disturbances in his developmental history.

After birth such variations in development may handicap the infant in some functions required by independent life, or they may be so minor that they do not become evident until the individual must meet the stresses of adult life. It is quite possible that all of us harbor within our bodies unknown defects that are the result of our early prenatal development, which we have compensated for in such a way that we live successfully in spite of them. The perfect human body is an abstraction of the anatomist, an ideal that is rarely if ever achieved during the long sequence of causally related events that determine our individual development.

One purpose of the study of human embryology is to give us some understanding of how variations in structure and function of the human body are caused. Such knowledge is important not only for scientists, but also for all intelligent adults whose biological responsibility is to produce and nurture the next generation. For this reason, we shall conclude this description of human development with a brief discussion of the variations that can occur in the biography of the unborn.

The most striking variation in human reproduction is the development of more than one infant within the same uterus at the same time. Man typically produces one offspring at a time, in contrast to many animals that usually have multiple reproduction. This is probably related to the relatively long period of development that precedes human birth, and to the relatively large size of the human infant at birth. As a rule where multiple births occur, the young are smaller in size and are born at an earlier stage in their development. In the human species multiple births occur relatively infrequently, with the likelihood of multiple births determined largely by the heredity of the parents. Twins occur in $1/87$ of human pregnancies, triplets in $1/7569$, quadruplets in $1/658,000$, and quintuplets once in 57 million births. The frequency of multiple births seems to vary with the age of the mother, and in different population groups or races.

Multiple births can occur as the result of two quite

different developmental processes. The most common cause, both in man and in other animals, is the formation and fertilization of more than one egg at a time. This type of multiple reproduction is the case in most animals that habitually give birth to litters. In man it is the most frequent cause of multiple births. More rarely, multiple births are the result of the separation of one fertilized egg into two or more embryos, with the time of separation varying all the way from the first cleavage to a relatively late stage in early embryonic development. This type of multiple reproduction is characteristic of a few animals, such as the armadillo, which always produces four identical offspring. In man it occurs less often than multiple egg formation, but when it does occur it also produces identical offspring.

Human twins may be used as an example of these two types of multiple reproduction (Fig. 27). It is common knowledge that twins may be of the same or opposite sex, and that they may or may not resemble each other more than do any two brothers or sisters. Twins that are formed when two eggs are released from the ovaries of the mother and both eggs are fertilized by different sperm are called fraternal twins. Such twins are no more similar to each other in heredity than any other children of the same parents. Both eggs pass down the Fallopian tubes and both embryos successfully embed in different parts of the uterine wall. The same process can give rise to fraternal triplets, quadruplets, or quintuplets. Embryos formed in this way will always have separate amniotic sacs and will usually have separate placentae, since both of these structures form from the developing egg. Sometimes, during growth of the placenta, the two placentae may invade the same part of the uterine wall and fuse with each other

145

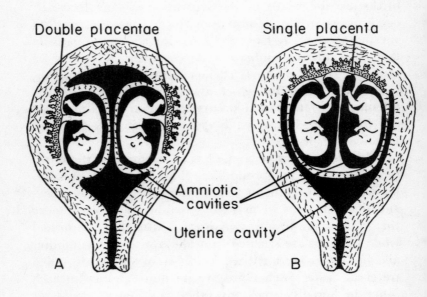

Double placentae   Single placenta

Amniotic
cavities

Uterine cavity

A   B

FIG. 27:

Two of the various possible relations of twins within the uterus.
A. Fraternal twins, with separate placentae and amniotic sacs.
B. Identical twins, with a common placenta but two amniotic sacs.

146

secondarily, so that at birth the two infants will be attached to the same placenta.

Identical twins, triplets, quadruplets, or quintuplets are formed from one egg, fertilized by one sperm, and they therefore have the same genes and similar chromosomes. For this reason they will always be of the same sex, and they will resemble each other in all of those aspects of structure or function that are determined primarily by heredity. However they may differ from each other in those features that are influenced by their environment during prenatal life, such as size and weight, degree of maturation of the organs, and the occurrence of variations. Such infants will be attached to one placenta, and they may or may not be enclosed in one amniotic sac, depending on whether the subdivision of the developing egg occurred before or after the amnion is formed. If the single fertilized egg separates into two cells after the first cleavage and both cells continue to develop normally, identical twins will be formed. If separation occurs later during cleavage, identical triplets, quadruplets, or quintuplets may be formed. The fact that such identical multiple offspring occur more rarely than do identical twins probably reflects the increasing difficulty of carrying out normal development by the daughter cells of successive cleavages, as well as the difficulties experienced when more than two embryos try to grow in the same uterus. The cause of such separation of the developing egg into two or more embryos, where only one is normally formed, is not yet known for man. It has been found that similar multiple identical embryos can be produced experimentally in some animals if the first two or four cells are separated mechanically, or if the developing embryo is constricted artifically.

Sometimes separation into two embryos occurs after the egg has embedded in the uterine wall, or even after the embryonic body has begun to form in the embryonic disc. When this occurs, the two embryos may be joined with each other through some part of the body that they share in common. Such embryos are less likely to survive throughout the complexities of embryonic and fetal life, so such conjoined twins rarely reach birth successfully. When they do, the degree of fusion between the two infants may vary all the way from a simple cord between their two abdomens to a lesser or greater fusion of heads, chests, abdomens, or legs. The two infants may have a common circulatory system, a single heart or liver, or they may share almost any of the major organs of the human body. The degree of separation or fusion reflects the time in development when twinning started. Early twinning, before the neural plate is formed, will result in relatively little fusion, whereas later twinning will affect mainly those organs whose precursors have not yet been determined in the developing egg. When the degree of fusion of the two infants is small, it can often be corrected surgically, but when it is extensive it becomes difficult if not impossible to separate successfully such conjoined twins. In theory such duplication during early development could produce more than two embryos, but the fact that such infants are not known suggests that such an extreme deviation from normal development must be fatal.

The fact that the human species commonly produces only one child at a time reflects in part the difficulties experienced when more than one embryo tries to develop within the uterus at one time. The food supplied by the mother's body must be divided between two or more rapidly developing embryos, and the space within the uterine cavity must be shared by the rapidly growing fetuses. These problems sometimes affect the development of the fetuses, so that one or more of them may be handicapped in growth and development. Even after successful birth one of the infants may be smaller and less mature than the others, and this "runt" can reach full normal growth and maturity only gradually after birth, when he can be given extra care and feeding.

Numerous other kinds of variations can and do occur during human development, ranging all the way from almost universal variations in the internal organs to visible variations in the form of the various external parts of the body. Mankind has always speculated about the cause of such variations, and during the course of history has offered various explanations of how deviations from normal development might occur. When knowledge of human development before birth was slight, man blamed all deviations from normal on the gods or devils who seemed to control all of his life and his world. In many cultures the birth of an abnormally developed child was believed to be an omen of future calamities. As the idea grew that most events in life on earth are not caused by remote and mysterious gods but by immediate and physical causes, men came to believe that the experiences of the pregnant woman marked her developing child through the effects of her body or mind on the fetus growing within her. The folklore of all cultures, including our own, is filled with legends of infants born with birthmarks or with abnormalities of the face, body, or limbs that were believed to be caused by some traumatic experience of the mother during pregnancy. This belief in the effect of maternal experiences on the developing fetus was used to urge pregnant women to deliberately seek good psychic experiences that might benefit the child's psychic development.

Such beliefs in the power of the mother to influence the development of her unborn child were gradually destroyed as scientists studied the actual processes of human development. The close similarity of the various steps in the development of the human embryo to comparable stages in the development of the embryos of other animals suggested that the processes of development are controlled inherently within the fertilized egg, and are not influenced by environmental forces. The fact that the same kind of variations or abnormalities seen in man can occur in the offspring of animals as different as fish, frog, reptile, or bird, where the embryo does not develop inside of the mother, offered further evidence against maternal influence on development. As the structure and physiology of the placenta were studied, belief in the protective action of the placental barrier developed. Doctors were able to reassure pregnant women that the events in their lives were unlikely to mark or otherwise affect their child. This reassurance freed the mother from many of her worries during pregnancy, and from the guilt she felt if her child proved to be less perfect than other children.

Modern medical care is based on the assumption that the development of the human embryo, fetus, infant, and child is controlled primarily by the genes with which each individual is endowed at fertilization. It has been shown that many of the variations or abnormalities that can occur during human development depend on the presence of certain inherited genes, or on the presence of irregular chromosome patterns. For example, the development of extra fingers or toes is known to be hereditary, while the development of mongolism, one of the most severe abnormalities that occur in human infants, is usually accompanied by the presence of an extra chromosome in the cells of the affected individual.

Many other human variations are also determined by the genes of the embryo. Perhaps the most thoroughly studied problem of the effect of heredity on human development has been the subject of the inheritance of blood types. Human blood cells show specific chemical properties that are determined by the genes of the individual, and the blood cells of different blood types provoke the formation of antibodies when they are introduced into the blood stream of individuals of different blood groups. Such antibodies then attack and destroy the opposite type of blood cell. Since the embryo inherits his genes from his father as well as his mother, his blood cells may be of a different type from those of his mother. It was pointed out earlier that blood cells of the fetus may pass through the placenta late in pregnancy and provoke the formation of antibodies in the mother's blood. These maternal antibodies may then affect the fetus that provoked their formation, and they may persist in the mother's blood and affect a later embryo developing within her uterus. This may occur especially if the mother has Rh negative type of blood cells while the fetus has Rh positive blood. In such cases the mother's antibodies may cause (but not invariably) abnormal development of the affected embryo, or the death of the fetus before birth, or severe anemia and jaundice in the infant immediately after birth. Since these effects of blood cell incompatibility between mother and child were discovered, it has become common medical practice to identify the blood type of every pregnant woman and of the father of her child, in order that the doctor may be forewarned of the possibility of difficulties for the child. Techniques have been developed that can help prevent or at least minimize the effects of such maternal-fetal incompatibility on the fetus and newborn infant.

Many of the complex processes through which the human embryo develops can be disturbed in various ways, so that the end result is the production of aberrant or abnormal structures in the fetus or infant. Development of a particular organ may be delayed or distorted at a critical time in its development, so that it never reaches the final form that characterizes the normally matured infant. The two heart septa may develop to the stages where the hole in each of them should be closed and then stop, leaving the infant with an incompletely divided heart. The fetal blood vessel that by-passes the lungs may fail to regress as it should after birth. In either of these cases, the infant will experience incomplete oxygenation of his blood, becoming a "blue baby." The growth and fusion of the two parts of the palate or the upper jaw may be too slow, or stop before it is completed, and the infant is born with a cleft palate or hare lip. The lower jaw may not grow rapidly enough during the second and third months, leaving the fetus equipped with an inadequate jaw. The kidney tubules may fail to join properly with the ducts that should drain the urine they excrete, and a cystic kidney will form. The fetal bones may find the supply of minerals needed for their ossification inadequate, so they fail to grow and ossify normally and the infant is born with rickets. All of these and other similar variations from normal development are believed to be caused by developmental arrest, as the result of some unknown force that delays or prevents each step in the developmental sequence from occurring at the proper time. The results of such delays may vary from temporary effects that are later corrected by growth or surgery to defects that seriously handicap the fetus or infant, sometimes to the point of death.

Other variations in normal development can result from an excess of growth of a particular organ or part of the embryonic body. The brain may grow too large to be contained in the skull, or the skull may become too large for safe passage through the birth canal. Extra organs may be formed, such as more than twelve pairs of ribs, or two mammary glands, two parathyroid glands, one uterus, or one bladder. Such developmental excess can be as much of a handicap to the fetus as developmental delays, since the normal development of the entire body depends closely on the balanced development of all its parts.

The purpose of mentioning such variations in an account of normal human development is not to distress the reader, but to point out the unfortunate fact that human development before birth is not a miraculously perfect process that can be depended on to always produce a normal human infant. Medical studies have shown that human development before birth can be and frequently is affected by events that occur within the environment in which the embryo and fetus grow. The old belief in the power of maternal experience to mark the developing infant was rightly destroyed by increased understanding of the manner in which the embryo develops and of the effectiveness of the placental barrier. But in recent years clinical and experimental studies have shown that some kinds of maternal experiences can affect the development of the embryo or fetus adversely. The purpose of these studies is to find out whether such adverse influences can be prevented or counteracted, so that they will not result in the birth of a handicapped infant.

It has been known for a long time that the diet of the mother affects the development of the embryo, fetus, and infant, both before birth and during nursing. The mother must provide all of the proteins, carbohydrates, fats, and minerals that are necessary to create the increasing mass of living cells that is her child. Experimental studies are beginning to show that she must also provide a specific, adequate amount of the vitamins that are needed for healthy functioning of living cells. It has been found that the developing embryo and fetus are far more sensitive to an inadequate level of the various vitamins than is the fully developed mother. Even though the mother may remain in good health throughout her pregnancy, the embryo may react to a low level of particular vitamins with abnormalities in its development. Moreover the evidence seems to suggest that a woman's diet before she becomes pregnant, particularly during the years of childhood and adolescence, may affect her ability to support the normal development of her child during pregnancy.

Similar clinical and experimental studies have shown that many substances other than foods can and do pass through the placenta and affect the development of the unborn child. Most of the drugs that are used for various purposes have been tested for safety only on adult, fully developed human beings. It has been shown that some of these drugs can pass through the placenta and have an adverse effect on the developing embryo or fetus. Viruses, bacteria, and other parasites that infect the mother sometimes pass through the placenta, and may infect the fetus with the same disease, or may upset the embryo at critical times so that abnormal development occurs. The recent evidence of the role of rubella (German measles) in sometimes causing blindness, deafness, or mental retardation in infants of mothers who experienced this relatively mild disease during the early months of their pregnancy has led to intensified study of the effect of diseases in the pregnant woman on human development. It has long been known that many serious diseases, such as small pox, tuberculosis, syphilis, typhoid fever and others, can be transmitted from mother to fetus. It has also been known for some time that unusual radiations, such as those produced by X-rays, radioactive isotopes, or nuclear explosions, can pass through the mother's body without apparently injuring her, yet have a profound and usually damaging effect on the sensitive, developing embryo.

All of these environmental influences may cause delays or aberrations of development if they become a part of the intra-uterine environment of the developing human embryo. So although we no longer warn pregnant women about traumatic experiences marking the infant, we must realize that the mother's body and the events that happen to and in it provide the environment of the developing embryo, and that the young human embryo is more sensitive to many environmental changes than is the mature mother.

It therefore becomes the individual responsibility of every woman to provide the best possible environment for the first home of her child. She can do this only if she knows what events in her life may affect the child's development. Worrying about the possibility of abnormal development will not promote the welfare of the child, but neither will ignorance of what these possibilities are. Knowledge of how human development occurs and how it can be affected must lead to a full realization of her own responsibility for providing the best possible conditions for her child during the nine months of its prenatal life.

It will never be possible to guarantee a perfect environment for human development, either before or after birth. But all parents want their children to be born normal and healthy. Knowledge of how this can be achieved is part of the responsibility of all adults, since ignorance never prevents natural events from taking place. The cost of ignorance of how human development occurs will be paid in human lives and human misery. Some of the damage that occurs during human development can be prevented only if we come to know the facts about the effects of heredity and environment on the embryo, fetus, and infant and then use our knowledge to improve the prenatal life of every human being. To be born without handicaps is the initial right of each individual man.

BIBLIOGRAPHY

Allan, F. D. *Essentials of Human Embryology*. Oxford Press. 1960.

Arey, L. B. *Developmental Anatomy*. W. B. Saunders Co. 1954.

Corner, G. W. *Ourselves Unborn*. Yale University Press. 1944.

Davies, J. *Survey of Research in Gestation and the Developmental Sciences*. Williams and Wilkins Co. 1960.

Dunham, E. *Premature Infants*. Hoeber-Harper Co. 1955.

Hadorn, E. *Developmental Genetics and Lethal Factors*. John Wiley and Sons. 1961.

Montagu, M. F. A. *Prenatal Influences*. C. C. Thomas Co. 1962.

Morison, J. E. *Foetal and Neonatal Pathology*. Mosby Co. 1952.

Patten, B. M. *Human Embryology*. McGraw-Hill Co. 1953.

Streeter, G. L. *Developmental Horizons in Human Embryos*. Carnegie Institution of Washington. 1951.

Windle, W. F. *Physiology of the Fetus*. W. B. Saunders Co. 1940.

INDEX

Page numbers in italics indicate illustrations.

Index

Genital tubercle, 73, 75, *76*
Gill clefts, 44, 47-48, *49*
Growth, 23, 44, 47-48, 66, 80-83, *81*, *84*, 117

Hair, 89-93, 99
Heart, 39, *43*, 45, *58*, 61-62, *94*, 129, 137-139, 152
Heredity, 13-14, 143, 147, 150-152
Hormones, 29, 30, 75, 78, 90, 132, 139
Hymen, 123

Immunity, 126
Implantation, *24*, 26
Inguinal canal, *120*, 121-122
Inner cell mass, *27*, 28
Intersex, 78
Intestine, *43*, 45 *58*, 70, 139

Kidney, *43*, 45, *58*, 71, 119, 139, 141, 152

Labia, *76*
Lanugo, 92, 118
Leg, *42*, 52-55, *54*
Liver, *43*, 45, *58*
Lungs, *58*, 61, 86, 113-114, 119, 129-130, 137-138

Mammary glands, 123-124
Maternal impressions, 149-150, 153-156
Maturation, 15-16, *17*, 18
Meconium, 97, 115
Menstruation, 21-22, 29-31
Mesonephros, *43*, 45-46, 72
Mouth, 48, 60
Mullerian ducts, 73, *74*, 123
Muscles, 55

Nails, 93, 118
Navel, 136
Nerves, 59, 90, 96-97, 109-113
Neural plate, tube, *27*, 36, 37
Notochord, *27*, 36

Ovary, 19, *20*, *24*, *58*, 72-73, *74*, 122-123
Ovulation, 21